Catch and Release

BECOMING A TEACHER WHO CHANGES LIVES

A Story by

Greg Dale

Lynn Owens

Mark Thomas

3DOT Publishing
Durham, North Carolina

Published by 3DOT Publishing, an imprint of
Excellence in Performance
7 Sinclair Circle
Durham, NC 27705

Design and production by BW&A Books, Inc.

ISBN 978-09755764-2-7
Library of Congress Control Number: 2017911118

First printing.

Contents

Foreword

This book was written for teachers by teachers. It was written as a love letter to all those who have been in the trenches, facing daily challenges and persevering through it all. It was written to express our sincere gratitude to you for caring about making a difference in the lives of your students and fellow teachers, and to share some of the wisdom that we have gained over the course of our respective teaching careers.

The process of writing this book was a huge learning experience. There were numerous teachable moments for each of us along the way. We talked for several years about writing some type of book for teachers. Finally, we got together and spent two days in a conference room discussing everything that we felt teachers needed to know and consider in their journeys. Our ideas included effective classroom management, healthy classroom culture, lesson planning, teacher development, and student motivation, to name a few. We literally had dozens of ideas for our book. As each new idea was discussed, one of us would share a story. The story came from either our own teaching experience or from an experience when we were in the role of student. Other times the story was of a teacher we had taught with or heard about from others. These stories made us laugh, made us sad, and made us think. We didn't plan for this process to occur. However, it happened very naturally.

As a result, it became clear that we should not write a textbook or a "how-to" book but rather a story. This book is meant to be a story about relationships between a mentor teacher and a novice teacher, between teachers and their students, between teachers and their colleagues, and between a married couple who are both teachers. We realized that the story is what's important. The lived narrative of teachers' lives matters. The examples of stories throughout this book are ones that we have experienced. They are based on real people whose names have been changed. The stories are also based on the various seasons teachers experience during their careers. We used a portion of a book on credible coaching written by Jeff Janssen and Greg Dale as a foundation for those seasons.

Whether you are a beginning teacher or someone who has been teaching for forty years, we hope you enjoy reading this book and that you are able to relate to the characters and their experiences. Our hope is that if you are just beginning your career, you will have a better roadmap to navigate the rewards and challenges of a teaching career. If you are an experienced teacher, our hope is that we affirm you and make you feel good about where you are as a teacher. Perhaps we will challenge you to think about how you might change how you interact with students and colleagues. That would be rewarding for us as well.

We thank you for the service you have provided over the course of your careers. We want you to know that the three of us have experienced many rewards and challenges throughout our teaching careers as well. And we want you to know that, like you, we continue to want to make a difference in the lives of others. We wish you the best as you continue to become a teacher who changes lives.

Part I

CHAPTER 1

The Surprise

Life is strange. Three months ago I would have never envisioned myself sitting in a massive ballroom at the Sheraton Hotel in Austin with my family, a few colleagues, and a handful of close friends waiting to receive the High School Teacher of the Year Award for the state of Texas. In short order I will have to offer an acceptance speech which I hope will be thoughtful, gracious, appreciative, reflective, and intelligent—all wrapped into less than fifteen minutes for a crowd of nearly 300 attendees recognizing excellence in teaching. Such is life at the moment for Nathaniel Bedford Speer . . . the guy who dreamed about being a teacher when he was growing up. This wasn't always a part of my boyhood dream, but as we age and mature I believe we take our dreams along for the ride.

Surprised? Definitely. Big time surprise, actually. Frankly, I'm aware of honors like this, but my reality was always that they didn't apply to me for so many reasons.

I've always seen teaching as giving as opposed to getting. Many times sports commentators and coaches will say that "the best game officiating goes unnoticed. Done well, the job seemingly disappears into the background as referees and umpires facilitate a contest as opposed to taking center stage." I have always liked that analogy and tried to emulate that concept in my classroom.

Heck, I didn't have a clue that the state teachers association knew Delmar Regional High School existed. We are the land of big ranches, cattle, mesquite trees, and windmills located along the Laguna Madre, which is one of the best places in the world to fly fish for redfish and trout. You can stand knee deep in salt water and have the time of your life catching as many fish as you can handle. We are 350 miles from Houston, four hours south of San Antonio, and sixty miles from the Mexican border. I've had a couple of months to get my head around receiving the award, but I must admit that the announcement was quite memorable.

It was mid-May and we were experiencing those "porch hot" days in South Texas, which to folks here means the ideal place to be includes a comfy chair, a cool drink, and some shade. Teaching and learning in these conditions can be challenging, but students and staff at Delmar are accustomed to dealing with plenty of challenges. That is what brought me here 30 years ago and keeps me here today.

I love an underdog and an underdog story. In many respects, winning this award feels that way to me. This award is as much about Delmar as it is about me. This school has afforded me a learning laboratory that allowed me to refine my craft and evolve into the teacher that I am today. That certainly was not always the case, but more on that later.

On that hot Thursday morning, our longtime Assistant Principal, Charlie White, sent out a memo to staff that there would be an assembly in the gym that day during last hour. Assemblies are seen as a blessing and a curse by many teachers. We understand it is important to build a positive culture and climate by bringing the students together for a presentation, activity, etc. There is also some angst when you lose up to 56 minutes of instructional time which will likely never be recovered.

But over the years, I have grown to appreciate that the classroom is not the only domain where learning takes place. I realized that sporting events, concerts, field trips, dances, lunch time, etc., were all classrooms, and it was up to us as educators to leverage every teachable moment over the course of a day.

With this in mind, I sent my 6th hour English class to the gym when the bell rang and seated myself, per usual, in the middle of the sophomore section. For the past few years my teaching schedule has been divided between English 10 and AP Literature. I like it because it gives me a chance to get to know many students as underclassmen and encourage them to take my AP class during junior or senior year.

I must admit that sitting in the gym that day, I had no idea of the topic for the assembly. I had been feverishly focused on preparing my AP Lit students for the upcoming national exam. So, I was glad that my last hour class was English 10 instead of one of my AP Lit classes.

Once everyone got seated, I noticed our Principal, Henry Rodriguez, standing with a couple of people I didn't recognize and our local media folks. He came to Delmar four years ago from a school about an hour south of us, not far from the border. The transition to Principal Rodriguez was a challenging time for me. I certainly respect him as a person and as an educator; my challenge was that he replaced Sharon Griffin. She was the longest tenured principal I've had since coming to Delmar, and she became an invaluable mentor and friend. I needed to grieve my loss, but I also needed to be supportive and open to growth.

Henry is in his mid-thirties, which was young for a principal when I started my career. Not anymore. It seems to be increasingly difficult to find quality educators who aspire to be administrators these days. That is not the case with him. He may have come to us rather green with little administrative experience, but he definitely has his heart and mind in the right place. He is passionate about education and not afraid to push our staff to improve.

Henry began walking to the podium stationed at mid-court. In front of him, facing the gathering, was a large chair which was decorated like a regal throne. The school marching band, affectionately referred to as "The Pony Express" since our school mascot is the Mustangs, was stationed on the floor as well. I was sitting in the bleachers thinking to myself that I must have missed the memo from Student Council about naming a Prom Queen or something. I have a bunch of seniors in class, though, and I don't remember any conversation or speculation on that topic.

At this point he addressed the crowd: "Dear students and staff. It is my pleasure to welcome you to a very special day here at Delmar High School. We are blessed and honored to have royalty among us! We have some special guests with us today to help celebrate. At this time I would ask all of you to help me welcome home one of our alumni, Luis Arguello. He helped make this celebration possible."

As soon as I heard Luis's name I was taken aback. He was a special student to me. He was a living, breathing reminder of why I became a teacher. Luis was possibly the best evidence I could ever offer if someone asked me, "Did you make a difference for kids?" In Luis's case I was confident that I could reply, "Yes. At least for this one!"

Luis graduated from Delmar and left us about eight years ago. He defied the odds and basically did a 180-degree turnaround with his life in just under three years of high school. He kept in touch with me on a pretty regular basis but I had no idea he was going to be at the assembly that day. He looked great. Like most of us, he had put on a few pounds and he no longer had that constant peach fuzz on his face that he would insist was the beginning of a great beard. That beard probably never materialized. He looked very professional, and I remember thinking how proud I was of him in that moment. Maybe he was receiving some sort of alumni award that he was too shy to tell me about. He may not have known himself based on what Henry just said.

At that point Luis stepped to the microphone. Behind him were all of the members of our Board of Education. Very rare. My curiosity was definitely piqued.

Luis addressed the audience: "Students and staff of Delmar, *mis compadres* and fellow Mustangs. My name is Luis Arguello. It seems like an eternity now, but eight years ago at this time I was a senior getting ready for the prom and then graduation. Just before graduation day I found out I was awarded a full academic scholarship to attend college. I was going to be the first member of the Arguello family to attend college. Actually, I was the first member of the Arguello family to graduate high school.

"I went off to college, and just over four years later I graduated. My degree was in education with a double major in History and Economics. I am now a certified teacher in the state of Texas. Many of my childhood friends were shocked because if you knew me growing up in Delmar you would have said that my future title would most likely be convict, not teacher. I thought I was all that and more. A *niño malo* just looking for trouble and thinking I had all the answers.

"Well, thankfully, that all changed for me here at Delmar High. It was in these classrooms, hallways, and playing fields that I learned how my choices were hurting me more than anyone else could have ever hurt me. The staff at Delmar High showed me that a different life was possible and helped me get there."

I sat there in the stands becoming emotional listening to Luis. I knew he understood this, but to hear him articulate so powerfully in front of 800 people made me beam with pride. It's really every teacher's dream. He so completely deserved this recognition he was about to receive!

"There were many people who helped me along the way, but there was one individual to whom I owe a special debt of gratitude. Mr. Speer, would you please stand up?"

The students and staff gave me a round of applause, but to tell you the truth, I was oblivious at the time. I certainly have an ego, and I truly appreciated Luis introducing me during his ceremony, but I would have been very happy to just get mentioned along with my colleagues.

"Many of you may know Mr. Speer, or 'Shake' as we used to affectionately refer to him, from English class. You might wonder how he got that nickname. I would like to take at least partial credit. My buddy Terrence and I were talking one day early in the fall of our senior year. We had Mr. Speer as a teacher and we were studying Shakespeare. Terrence said Mr. Speer was his favorite teacher and it seemed to him that great teachers deserved nicknames. I agreed and said we should call him 'Shake' because he was Mr. Speer teaching Shakespeare. Terrence loved it and we decided he would be referred to as 'Shake' from that day forward. Luckily Mr. Speer didn't object the first time I called him by that name. He just smiled, and you could tell he kind of liked it and it caught on with the other kids.

"If you haven't had him for class, go see your counselor and find out if you can sign up next semester. I was assigned to his English 10 class my sophomore year and I still thank God for that gift every day. I never read a book before entering his class. Now when I say never read a book, I really mean it. I had plenty of teachers tell me I had natural ability, but I was always too cool for school. I was the class clown and class bully all wrapped into one. Sleeping, disrupting, chasing *chicas*, anything to swim upstream. That was me. I had a reputation to uphold, and because I was good at being bad, it was a 24/7 gig."

I was smiling as I listened to Luis describe himself back in high school. I was also really beginning to feel awkward standing there in the middle of the crowd with all eyes on me.

"Starting school that fall was really no different except for Mr. Speer's class. I was coming off a wild summer which included drinking, drugs, stealing, and multiple run-ins with *la ley* and *la policia*. That is until I came across Mr. Speer. I got to his class and began to put on my normal act. The first time I did one of my patented disruptive moves which, invariably, would upset the vast majority of other teachers I had ever had, Mr. Speer looked at me and replied, 'Luis, I am excited to have you in my class because I think you can make me a better teacher. Can I ask something of you? Would you be willing to help me become a better teacher and help this group of people to become a better class? Please? You could be so valuable to me, to all of us actually. Let's talk after class during lunch. Go ahead for now and get your book out. Thanks so much!'

"I remember that first lunch period like it was yesterday. I waited until after class dismissed. Mr. Speer asked me to sit down so we could talk. He didn't sit behind his desk though. He didn't sit on top of a desk in order to have a power position over me either. I learned that from a police show and actually had a number of cops and teachers try to intimidate me using that. It never worked. No, Mr. Speer came around and sat right next to me. He shook my hand and thanked me for staying, and then he said something that had an incredible impact on me. I later wrote it down and keep it on my desk at school today as a reminder about the importance of the choices I make.

"He calmly looked at me and said, 'Luis, you are tremendously powerful because you have the ability to choose. However, you do not have the power to control the consequences of those choices, so I suggest that you learn to choose wisely. You have quite the reputation with many adults in our school and the community. But, as far as I am concerned the past doesn't matter to me. We just met each other this morning. It would be unfair to both of us if either one of us made judgments on the other one based on what others say. I believe to truly know someone; you have to personally get to know him or her.'

"He told me I possessed leadership qualities. He also reminded me that great leaders have willing followers, and great leaders are subject to the consequences of their choices.

"He asked me what I needed from him in order to make a quality effort in his class. I couldn't believe it. I had been told what I was going to do a thousand times, but no one since elementary school had ever asked me what I needed. I blurted out, 'Respect,' and he looked straight into my eyes and said, 'Done!'

"He went on to tell me in that first meeting that he would never expect me to place my trust in him from just this conversation. He asked me to give him a shot, because the definition of trust is confidence based on consistency over time. If he failed to live up to his end of the bargain, he would give me a passing grade regardless of my work. If he held up his end of the deal then I would strive to do my best in his class. With that he stood up, extended his hand and thanked me for my time. I shook his hand and walked to the lunchroom wondering what just happened and who was this guy, Mr. Speer.

"Let me tell you, the rest of that year and the next few years he definitely held up his end of the bargain. What I quickly found out was that Mr. Speer cared about all of his students. He didn't just know their names, he got to know them. He had high standards and expectations, but he also understood that life happens, and learning isn't confined to a textbook or classroom. He saw the best in me and taught me to take personal responsibility and accountability for anything less.

"He invited my mother in after the first month of school to tell her how much he enjoyed having me in class and how well I was doing. She almost fell over. The only time she ever heard from school in the past was when I was suspended for fighting, skipping, or showing disrespect to one of my teachers or a classmate. He told other teachers and the administration that if they had any issues with me in school to please contact him. He would then meet with me to discuss the situation. He would ask me to reflect. He would offer advice as to how to resolve the issue, and then he would ask me to provide an example which would validate that I understood the proper choice moving forward. He would refer to these as teachable moments. Once I had demonstrated mastery of the concept, he expected me to handle it successfully in the future or face the negative consequences of my actions because he constantly reminded me that choices have consequences and I control my choices.

"Ever since sophomore year, Mr. Speer has always been there for me. Crazy thing is I discovered over time that he has been there for many kids from Delmar. The staff here at Delmar is all about kids. It may not always be perfect, but that is how relationships happen. It wasn't always perfect for Mr. Speer and me, but that was the beauty of the journey. It was because of him that I decided to become a teacher. I felt that the best way to honor his contributions to my life would be to try and do the same for someone else. Mr. Speer, I can never repay you, but please consider this as a sign of my lasting appreciation and respect, sir!"

With that Luis stepped away and Henry stepped back to the microphone. "Mr. Speer, please remain standing if you would. At this time it is my privilege to introduce Dr. Robert Pearson, the Executive Director of the Texas State Teachers Association. Let's give Dr. Pearson a warm Mustang welcome!"

Dr. Pearson stepped to the podium. "Thank you, Principal Rodriguez. Greetings from Austin. It is my pleasure to be here today. I think we have some other guests in attendance as well . . . please come on out, folks."

Right then from the corner of the gym I saw my wife and two kids emerge seemingly out of nowhere. Ryan, my oldest, had been in Dallas for the last five years, working in banking. Ginny, my baby, was supposed to be off at school studying to be a pediatrician someday. Both of them were smiling ear to ear while escorting my wife, Suzy, to the podium area. At this point I was severely out of sorts and feeling vulnerable, which was an unaccustomed state for me. Dr. Pearson went on.

"Some of you may think I am here for Mr. Arguello, who deserves our recognition for the wonderful achievements he began here at Delmar and continues today in his own classroom in the Dallas Independent School District. In actuality, I am here because of Mr. Arguello. He felt like he needed to share his story with us. Not for personal recognition but to honor and recognize the role that a teacher played in changing his life. That is what brings me here today. Without great teachers it would be difficult to have great students, let alone great individuals who contribute successfully to our great state and the nation.

"I'm here today to celebrate the power and impact that great teachers have on the lives of students every single day. Students like yourselves and Mr. Arguello over there. It needs to be recognized, and I'm certainly proud to be the one who gets to do it today! Mr. Speer, would you please come down here. Ladies and Gentlemen, I would proudly like to introduce all of you to the 2016 Texas Teacher of the Year . . . Mr. Nathaniel Speer!"

Over the last couple of months I have tried to remember what happened after that. My knees were shaking as I descended the bleachers. They sent two students to escort me while other students rolled out the red carpet leading to the throne and center court. I was crying. My wife and kids were crying and the band was playing. I met my family at the carpet, and as we began the walk together to center court, there was one thing I remember vividly. As we were walking forward I looked up to see Luis waiting for me. He had this glowing look of satisfaction. I've seen it before, but this time it was different.

As we embraced, he leaned over and whispered in my ear, "I believe this is another teachable moment. You always encouraged us to take the time to acknowledge those who have invested in us in some way. Thanks for being my teacher, Mr. Speer!"

That was just over two months ago. Tonight I am at the Texas State Teachers Association Gala Dinner in Austin surrounded by family, some close friends, colleagues, and hundreds of other folks connected to teaching in some manner. This evening I will be formally presented with the teaching award. It is also incumbent upon me to articulate some words which are hopefully perceived as gracious, thoughtful, and relevant. What have I learned since that day in our gym last May? Hopefully many things, but one affliction I have been battling is the "disease of me."

I often talk to my family and students about this topic. In today's society, many individuals seem completely enamored with themselves. Self-worth and popularity are seemingly measured via Twitter, Instagram, Facebook, YouTube, Tumblr, Pinterest, and Google. Role models and heroes for many have now shifted to the cast of *Jersey Shore*, *Real Housewives*, the Kardashians, *Love and Hip Hop*, and *Honey Boo Boo*, just to name a few. Frankly it has scared the hell out of me for a while now, and one of my biggest fears is to receive notoriety without demonstrating humility, appreciation, and responsibility for improving the world moving forward.

I have recently been experiencing a bit of schizophrenia in that regard. My Kardashian side is definitely enjoying the attention (which I must admit is pretty nice at times). My inner Thoreau keeps tugging at me to live simply and find my Walden away from the spotlight. My students refer to it negatively as "ASB," which means attention seeking behavior. Ironically, not cool if you seem like you are working hard to get it, but really cool if you do get it. Currently my goal is to remain mindful of staying self-aware and balanced. I'm not sure this award is going to get me a private parking spot at school or more students signing up for my AP classes just to bask in my intellectual afterglow. I must admit, though, it has definitely put some gas in my tank and motivated me to use my newly-minted status to advocate for the teaching profession.

I have also come to the realization that not everyone will be happy for me receiving this honor. I also think my future efforts will likely take place under a microscope of sorts for advocates and adversaries alike. That's just the way life is in society today. I think there is something innate in our human nature that drives us to pass judgment on things. I also think that in our country, school teachers seem to be a prime target for criticism. I think the only prerequisite needed to pass judgment on teachers is that you once participated in formal schooling in some fashion. I would also include school coaches under that umbrella as well because everyone feels as though they are qualified to coach. Present day circumstances tend to pull scabs off previous emotional wounds, which then allow some individuals to find the familiar axe they are so used to grinding and have at it.

David Ballard was the third principal I worked under in my career. Nice guy, smart guy, but he was tired both personally and professionally. He knew he was a "short-timer" who could retire at any time. I think that empowered him at times to be painfully honest with some parents he felt went over the line as far as being judgmental. David didn't discriminate, though, because he would take the same approach with teachers who he felt were overly judgmental. It made for great emotional theater at times. Often he would say, "In life some folks are just an opinion looking for an issue." Another one of his favorite axioms was, "Some people go to a car race hoping to see a crash." I was pretty young at the time, but over the years I have grown to appreciate David's wisdom when it comes to the human condition. My mom used to say the same thing about people who watch soap operas on television. "Focusing and passing judgment on other people allows some folks to avoid looking at themselves." Over the years I have pretty much found both of them to be correct.

Now I'm sure that in previous generations the concept of judgment-passing took place as well. What did not take place, though, was the ability for people to publicly amplify their opinions via the social media platforms we have today. It used to be confined to the grocery store, local newspaper, bowling alley, local bar, or church. Now it just takes anyone with a device and a Wi-Fi connection to share their thoughts and feelings with the entire world. Like the entire world even cares. I'm all for free speech and the First Amendment. Unfortunately, the First Amendment doesn't state that one should also be required to sign his or her name to an opinion. As an English teacher I love citing sources for accuracy and ownership. I wish it was a national law!

It seems like anyone who ever attended school feels like that makes them qualified to pass judgment on the quality of teachers. It is with some trepidation that I look forward to finding out if the old axiom "Heavy is the head that wears the crown" is true. What the last couple of months have really given me is some time to essentially look into the mirror and determine how I can ensure that I like and respect the person I see. I have always attempted—granted, imperfectly many times—to follow through on my word. I know more people will be watching and listening now to see if I'm the real deal or just "all hat and no cattle" as we are prone to say about pretenders, frauds, and showboats. On in ten minutes.

It's really nice that so many people from Delmar made the trip. I know it wasn't easy for everyone, and some of them changed vacation plans to be here. I think this is probably the first time some of those guys have worn a suit and tie in years. Suzy looks amazing tonight. I'm a lucky guy.

I sure wish mom and dad were here to see all of this. Dad would certainly give me a hard time that everyone is making such a fuss over me. Mom would be her usual glowing self and make such a big deal about it.

I know I'm ready for this speech, but I'd be much more comfortable talking about Jane Austen or correcting verb tenses in a five-paragraph essay. But, this will be fun. Wish me luck!

"Ladies and Gentlemen, it is with great pride that I present to you our 2016 State of Texas High School Teacher of the Year, Mr. Nathaniel Speer!"

CHAPTER 2

The Speech

Good evening. I'm accustomed to speaking in front of people on a daily basis, but I must admit that my audience is normally much younger and smaller in numbers. I currently teach two courses which occur multiple times every day. I like this arrangement because it allows me to reflect on my teaching, and then quickly make modifications to my lesson plan for the later periods to improve learning. Now I know what you are all going to say: "I think that's great, but I would certainly hope that my child has Mr. Speer's class after lunch instead of early in the morning!"

There's a bit of truth to that line of thinking. However, what it really means for all of you tonight is I have been given special permission to give this acceptance speech two more times this evening, later in the program. So no worries. If you feel like I have swung and missed at the conclusion of this oratorical endeavor, remain calm in knowing that I have two more swings at the plate to either get a hit or strike out. Welcome to the life of a teacher! Five shows a day, every day for 180 days, and in my case, multiplied over the last 30 years of my professional life. It sounds daunting when one does the math, but I truly love it, and I am so grateful once again to be here this evening.

This event honors teaching and the profession of education, but we would be remiss if we didn't include the concept of learning as well. Learning is the intended outcome of teaching. One struggles to exist without the other. It would be like a father asking his son to play a game of pitch instead of catch. So with that in mind, let me give you the lesson plan for the next few minutes we will spend together. Here are the learning targets:

1. The learner will be able to define the terms appreciation, passion and commitment.
2. The learner will be able to share a real-life example of each term.
3. In the future, the learner will be able to independently apply and model these concepts and actions successfully in their own lives.

Okay, we are now going to do a quick formative assessment so I can check for understanding. As a teacher this means that I need to be sure that everyone gets what it is I'm looking for in the lesson. We will use thumbs to accomplish this. I will count to three, and at that point if you feel you understand the learning goals please give me both thumbs up. If you feel pretty good but not quite sure, thumbs sideways. If you are lost, thumbs down. Here we go: one . . . two . . . three! Oh, very good. Easily over 90% clarity on the goals. If you have someone next to you who was unsure in the least, please be sure to assist them as we move forward.

Appreciation

One thing that I have always tried to impress upon my students is for them to recognize and thank those people who help them along the way in life. I know I am being recognized with a teaching award this evening, but it is certainly safe to say that I would not be here if I wasn't able to recognize early on the importance of being a student and the value of lifelong learning. In my case, I feel this accolade exemplifies someone who began as a novice and now has reached a level of strong competence and mastery.

My professional journey up to this evening could best be summed up in the Beatles lyric, "the long and winding road." I shudder when I think of my early years as a teacher and what my poor students had to endure from an idealistic educator who, at the time, didn't know what he didn't know. I agree with Malcolm Gladwell when he shares his theory that it takes 10,000 hours of practice before one can truly master a skill or craft. I have definitely put in the time, but I would add that mastery or improvement also requires the investment of others along the way through modeling, coaching, mentoring, and motivating. I have been fortunate to have people like that in my life, and it is most important to me that I acknowledge and thank them this evening.

It starts with my wife Suzy and my two children, Ryan and Ginny. Suzy certainly wasn't my first teacher, but it is safe to say that she has been my best teacher. She has taught everything from 1st grade through 8th grade for many years, and take it from me, folks, she is a far better educator than I will ever be. What she does with those children each day is amazing. It takes such patience to teach at the elementary and middle school levels. I have a great deal of respect for Suzy and all of the other teachers out there that teach at those levels. I marvel at her skills as a mother, daughter, sibling, friend, and partner. I learned about romance, love, and lifelong partnership through my relationship with Suzy. When people who know me meet Suzy for the first time, it's not uncommon for them to scratch their heads wondering how I am with her. Using a football analogy, many guys will look at me, smile and say, "Nathaniel, you really out-kicked your coverage with Suzy!" I always smile back and say, "Without question." It is also without question that I would not be here tonight if it weren't for her. It is with great respect and true appreciation that I am able to publicly acknowledge her this evening for all of her support, guidance, companionship, and unconditional love along the way. Honey, I love you and thanks so much!

On to my two children, Ryan and Ginny. There is little doubt I had no idea about parental love and commitment until I was in the hospital watching my wife give birth to our own children. Life has never been the same for me since those two days, and I mean that in the best ways possible. Ryan, as the oldest I need to now publicly apologize because, in reality, I had no idea of what I was doing as a father. You were our initial launch, and thank God for your mother because it was definitely trial and error for me on a daily basis. I must say that looking back you did make things very easy on us though. You were an enjoyable baby who evolved into a wonderful boy. You followed that up by becoming a fine man.

Ginny, my baby girl, I know there have been times in your young life where you think I may have been too strict when it comes to fashion, dating, curfews, etc. I want to encourage you to please direct any frustrations or anger you may have towards God and not me, because he was the one who decided to give a daughter to a father who teaches high school boys for a living. I'm sorry, honey, but it's just not my fault! I'm sure your social life is much easier now that you are off at college. I would like to say the same goes for me, but I can't because you will always be my baby girl.

To both of you, I want to say thank you for your patience and understanding with me. I certainly didn't have all of the answers as a father, and I made plenty of mistakes along the way. But I did my best to be loving, ethical, kind, persistent, and optimistic. It is my hope that the two of you would say you learned a few things from me growing up, because I certainly received an education from both of you as your father. To both of you I'll share one of my favorite quotes pertaining to parenting: "I can't guarantee that I will be here for the rest of your lives, but I can guarantee that I will love you both for the rest of mine!"

Continuing with the topic of appreciation, I would be remiss if I didn't take a few moments to acknowledge my parents. Dad passed away three years ago, and Mom left us almost ten years ago now. Many folks would describe them as working class parents, which normally means that they lacked formal advanced education. That is technically true but certainly not indicative of their intelligence. The term "working class" to me in regards to them means two things: they both possessed a tremendous work ethic, and they also handled themselves and others with class and dignity. It seems to me that we could all learn a thing or two from the example my parents provided.

Dad left high school to join the military and Mom got her diploma before taking a factory job as a seamstress in Philadelphia. They married a year after my dad came home. Even though they lacked post-secondary education, they had a lifelong belief that education would be the pathway to a professional career. They were convinced it could offer greater financial security in life for my sister Patty and me. Dad and Mom both worked, sometimes multiple jobs to provide for us and help put us through college.

I became a teacher and they were thrilled because they had a deep respect for education and the profession of teaching. Patty obviously listened better when my folks talked about the financial opportunities because she studied medicine and is a very talented doctor still living in the Philadelphia area.

My first teachers were my parents. They created a learning environment and culture based on what my dad called the Fundamental Five: respect, accountability, trust, grit, and optimism. We all know respect, accountability, and trust have long been passed down from one generation to the next as important values. However, as we know from the research on grit by Angela Duckworth and optimism by Martin Seligman and others, my dad was ahead of his time with his emphasis on those two values.

I strive to include these values in my classroom every day. Like all great teachers, they made the learning goals and vision very clear to us. They modeled learning to my sister and me by the way they led their lives every single day. They knew we were watching them all of the time, and they owned the responsibility that came with the job of parent.

As we grew, our daily lives became the classroom they managed as teachers, and as we got older they would give us more responsibility to own our choices. Looking back, their instructional process and learning strategies were brilliant, and time has proven that they were effective as well. I wish my parents could be here this evening because the highest compliment I could pay to both of them would be to say thank you for being the two of the finest teachers I have ever had in my lifetime.

The last group I want to recognize under the term "appreciation" is all of the colleagues and students I have worked with over the years. There are far too many to count and far too many to name, but I need to tell all of you that I can honestly say that I've tried to learn something from every one of you over the years. Now let me qualify that by saying what I have learned may not have always come from a positive encounter, but I tell my students that every situation and interaction offers a teachable moment of some kind, and the wise individual extracts knowledge whenever and wherever possible.

As I reflected on offering my appreciation to this particular group, it dawned on me that it is somewhat like grading a test or paper in class. You certainly want everyone to rate highly and get an "A," but in reality there is always a span between those who got it sooner than those who did not. I can honestly say that I have not always loved or admired all of my colleagues. However, I do feel the vast majority of the educators I have interacted with care deeply about kids. I feel the same way about the students I have had over the years as well. There is one big caveat to that. Teachers chose the profession and have a responsibility for performance, professional growth, commitment, etc. Students do not have the same control when it comes to different variables in their lives. They are also 14–18 years old and still need guidance. They are supposed to make mistakes, and adults are supposed to correct them and teach them how to move forward successfully.

I will share a personal aside as a teacher who became an expectant parent. This was passed on to me as one of those urban legends by a couple of humorous veteran educators just after I was married. Their advice to me was to have kids as soon as possible. I obviously took the bait and asked for further rationale. They told me that attempting to name a child for a teacher can be a very unique experience. If you have had a colleague or student that may have been a challenge for you in some way, it can tend to create a negative association which automatically rules that name out of the process. Couple that with the fact that I doubled down by marrying a teacher as well, and they said Suzy and I better get busy because the pool would dwindle rapidly! I'm happy to report that their theory, although somewhat true and certainly entertaining, had no negative impact on us choosing Ryan or Ginny.

I could easily spend all night naming those individuals who have made a powerful impact on me over the course of my career, but instead I will just toss out a blanket thank you to all of my students and colleagues, both past and present, for allowing me to learn from each and every one of you.

The second term I feel is appropriate to share with you tonight is Passion. It is such a crucial component of success for all of us. I apologize if I sound like I am on my "soap box" for a few minutes on this topic.

Passion

It is a term that resonates strongly within me. Henry David Thoreau once said, "The mass of men [and women] lead lives of quiet desperation." I certainly believe that to be true in many respects. I believe that many people today substitute passive for passion, then add the term aggressive as well. What I mean by that is many people are passive when it comes to finding or pursuing a passion in life. Many of those same people feel the world owes them something, and they then become aggressive in their complaints and criticisms about certain aspects of our society. In recent years, the teaching profession has increasingly become a target and an excuse for the mass of people leading lives of quiet desperation. It seems too easy to blame teachers and education for their shortcomings. It is also far too easy to throw out June, July, and August as the three best reasons to become a teacher. That just isn't true. I know there are exceptions who take advantage of the system and live for their three months off in the summer, but every profession has individuals who take advantage of the system.

I'm on a roll here, but I also believe that far too many people seem to get their self-worth from the device that is attached to their hand the vast majority of the time. I encourage my students to avoid allowing their self-esteem to fluctuate by the minute, hour, day, or month. Social media has done that to us. Reality television has become the "soap opera" of our time. I would contend that our society would have a very difficult time defining and identifying heroes and positive role models that aren't associated with reality television, highly adversarial politics, individuals who use cynicism, cruelty, negative rumor, innuendo, and personal attacks.

I'm passionate about teaching, which means I'm passionate about young people and having them grow up to be ethical, empathetic, and committed citizens in our society. I think it is incumbent upon all of us here tonight to do some self-reflection in order to review and recommit to our passions in life. There is currently an attack on schools and the profession of teaching in our society, which has been growing in fervor for a number of years. If we are truly passionate about this profession then we need to act like it and start being our own best advocates—because if we don't, then we are choosing to join the mass of men and women leading lives of quiet desperation. The ones who choose to complain as opposed to commit. That is not how I was raised. It isn't how I raised my children or teach my students, and it will not be how I choose to live my life moving forward.

Okay, I'm stepping down from my "soap box" now. Well, actually I will keep one foot on as I address the third term I mentioned at the beginning. I want to talk with you about commitment.

Commitment

I have now spent over a half-century on this earth. I have been a teacher for the last 30 of those years. While I'd like to believe that many people are well-intentioned, the greatest challenge for most folks is in walking their talk. It is going from vision to reality, in knowing what to do, but more importantly how to get it done. This knowing/doing process becomes the essence of what great teachers are able to accomplish in life. I also think greatness should be defined as not just doing something once, but being able to replicate the process on a repeated basis.

Give me a farmer who has a record of strong annual crop production in spite of variable weather conditions. Give me a coach who has demonstrated over time that he or she has developed a program as opposed to a team. Give me a restaurant owner who has added locations and still managed to maintain the quality of food and service which made the original store a hit in the first place. Examples like that don't happen by accident, they happen through commitment.

Receiving an honor like this is certainly a wonderful thing, but I cannot let it serve as a destination in my professional journey as a teacher. I actually see it as quite the contrary. I now believe, more strongly than ever, that it calls upon me to make a further commitment to our profession.

I want to take the time to acknowledge Luis Arguello. I found out that Luis nominated me for this award. I am proud to say that he is a former student of mine. I am honored that I can call him a fellow teaching colleague and most privileged that I can consider him a true friend.

I was humbled when Luis credited me as his motivation for becoming a teacher. He has obviously found his passion, and I cannot tell you the satisfaction that brings me. I know he is appreciative by the kind words he has shared about me. I also know he is committed because he took the extra time to go through the nominating process and physically attend festivities such as these. To this old teacher it is gratifying evidence that Luis learned his lessons well! Thank you so much, Luis. I am so grateful and proud of you.

Tonight I need to make a couple of commitments to all of you. They are not for you per se. They are really for me. I want to make them publicly to take my sense of commitment to another level. I'll be darned if I ever see any of you again someday and have to tell you that I didn't walk my talk! Here we go.

I realize that this honor comes with a "bully pulpit" of sorts, which should allow me multiple opportunities to vigorously advocate and defend education and the profession of teaching. You have my word that from this day forward I will strive to be a champion in that regard.

I am committed to staying true to what I try to do every day. I will strive to inspire curiosity, challenge others, and promote critical thinking and collaboration. I want to do it all in an environment of unconditional care and respect for my students. But that doesn't mean I will always like the choices they may make. In life, we all must learn to be accountable for our individual choices. That is the foundational philosophy I strive to model in my classroom and my life in general.

I certainly don't claim to have it all figured out at this stage of my life, but the old axiom "experience is the best teacher" certainly has some merit, because I promise you there were few indicators early in my career that an honor such as this would be in my future! We all start as novices in a variety of pursuits. We possess particular aptitudes, talents, or other variables which impact the rate in which we advance to levels of competency and mastery. And, just as I tell my students every day, anyone can improve if they are willing to dedicate themselves to practice their craft. Persisting through failure, seeking mentors and coaches to improve, and self-reflecting on the journey are keys to mastering one's craft. The fact that I am here tonight receiving this honor offers ample evidence that ugly ducklings can indeed turn into swans.

I have also come to the realization that it is not enough for me to just motivate someone like Luis to become a teacher. It is wonderful that someone like Luis wanted to become a teacher, but how can I help a young teacher to become a successful veteran teacher with a passion for students and education? Research shows that far too many beginning teachers are leaving the profession in the first five years of their career. That needs to be addressed, and I am committed to doing my part. In the last month or so my school hired a new teacher in my department. She is fresh out of college, and I want to do everything in my power to help her be successful. So tonight, with my principal in attendance, I am making a formal request to serve as her mentor teacher. I hope that is okay, Boss!

In conclusion, I want to thank all of you from the bottom of my heart. This whole experience has been something I'll cherish and never forget. This experience will also be something which will serve to motivate me even more in the future. Now, I know that you're all thinking the bell is going to ring very soon on Mr. Speer's speech and he won't have time to give us any homework! Sorry folks. There's always enough time, and there are three things I'm assigning each of you to do.

1. Think about someone you appreciate in your life and take a few moments over the next couple of days to call him or her. Write that person a note or have a personal conversation where you genuinely thank him or her for investing in you. I can assure you it will make that person's day and will require very little effort on your part.
2. Take a few minutes in the near future to reflect and determine three things you are passionate about in your life and what you will do to pursue them moving forward.

3. Lastly, make a commitment to those passions by sharing them publicly with friends or family who care about you and love you enough to hold you accountable for making progress on your commitments.

God Bless the United States of America, the Great State of Texas, and the profession of teaching and education. Class dismissed!

CHAPTER 3

The First Day

Meghan

August 24

I'm so excited, I can't sleep. Finally, after 12 years of school and four years of college, my first day of teaching begins tomorrow. I've waited for this day for years. And tomorrow, all the hard work, waiting, lesson planning, practicum experiences and classes I took are over. Tomorrow, they will call me teacher.

Technically it's only the Back to School staff meeting, but it's a start. I'm so excited to meet my fellow teachers. I'm also anxious about this. What will they be like? Will they like me? Will I like them? Will they really care about me and my success? Will they be patient with me? Will they encourage me? Will they expect me to be just like them? Am I even capable of that? Am I supposed to be like them? Oh my goodness, I've got to get some sleep.

And what about the students? It wasn't so long ago that I was one of them. What will they be like? Are kids today the same as when I was that age? How can I not know that? What do I remember from those child development classes, from those elementary, middle, and high school methods classes? I can't seem to remember anything. Will the kids like me? Will I like them? What if they liked their former teacher so much that they don't even give me a chance? What if nobody learns anything? What if I can't control them? What if I can't do this? What have I gotten myself into? Is it too late to back out?

I am excited. I am afraid. I think I'm ready. I'm not sure. I want to be like all of my best teachers. I want to make a difference. I want to make my students feel like I felt in those classes with my best teachers. I really need to get some sleep.

Nathaniel

August 25

Today dawns and I am up, awake, and ready to go without an alarm. As the years have gone by, my reliance on the alarm clock to wake me up has diminished. Something about age, circadian rhythms, and routines keeps me going like a well-oiled machine. Today, just like every weekday for the past 30 years, I wake up, get ready to go, and head out the door to the best job on the planet. And today, I will welcome a "wet behind the ears" newbie into the profession.

Although I've never met her, we already share much in common. If we didn't, neither of us would be here today. Most everyone going into the teaching profession shares similarities. We all love learning and we all love kids no matter the age. We probably enjoyed our own schooling and had good teachers. We loved those good teachers and paid close attention to what they did and who they were. Those were the teachers who believed in us and made a difference in our lives. Sometimes, we had a teacher who wasn't so good or at least wasn't so good for us, and that experience only served to fuel the fire to become a better teacher. So today, although I've not yet met her, I'm fairly certain that the teacher that I'll be mentoring is like that. She cares about kids, and wants to make a difference in the lives of students. I can hardly wait to get to school and today, call her teacher.

The drive to school finds my mind wandering back over the course of my career. Yes, I wanted to make a difference and I wanted teaching to be my career, but I remember times when it was hard. Life became challenging when hard things happened at school, at home, and in my life. I would like to think that I was always a great teacher dedicated to my craft. Sometimes that was certainly true. Other times, nothing could be further from the truth.

What I realize now over the course of this long career is that there were different seasons. Somehow, I have thrived, and at times survived through these seasons. And as I pull up to my school, with the students, the faculty, and the staff that I love so much, I realize the greatest lessons I can teach to this new teacher will be about those seasons. Without understanding this, she will struggle, she will doubt, and she might not survive. The most important decision that I will make today is to care enough to tell her the truth about teaching. She needs to know the good, the bad, and the seasons.

For me, there has always been something special about Back to School. There is a certain anticipation that begins to build in early August as summer is winding down. Our world seems to think so too. The television commercials advertising Back to School specials on kids' clothing and shoes have been on the air for several weeks now. The lists of school supplies needed for children have been sent home to parents and posted at local stores. The preparation is in full swing by the third week of August, and today I awake with renewed energy and vigor to get to school.

The annual Back to School staff meeting is today, and the renewed energy and vigor goes beyond just that meeting. There is a certain predictability and rhythm to these initial staff meetings. The routine of these over the years has sometimes lulled me into going through the motions. That is, until we move into our department meetings and then to time spent in my classroom. That is my favorite part. I cannot control much, but I can control what happens in my classroom. And sometimes, what happens is magic. But I digress.

The faculty and staff have gathered in the library this morning. I find myself arriving a bit early again in anticipation that today will be the start of something new. I am met by others who are eager to get to work, most of whom I recognize, but as always, there are a few new faces. I wonder which one belongs to my new mentee. As we begin to mingle, reconnecting after several months away, more teachers and staff members arrive. Some look ready and excited. Some look like they are still in summer mode.

As usual, there is the typical array of breakfast items laid out along one wall. Of course, there is coffee, but this year there is an exciting addition. There sits a Keurig with a wide variety of single serving choices. There are also various flavored creamers and sugars available. I find this amusing and remember when we were thankful to have just one giant pot of never-ending black coffee. We never seemed to care what it tasted like. It provided the added boost we needed to get the day started. There are also the assortment of carb-loaded pastries and muffins surely waiting to provide us with that sugar high followed by the sugar low by 10 A.M. I see there are more healthy choices this year. We have fruit and yogurt. Happy as that makes me, I grab my usual, enormous blueberry muffin. As I look around, I am reminded of how much has changed and yet again, how much has stayed the same.

Without really any call to attention, the mingling sea of faculty and staff slowly begins to find a seat in some kind of orderly fashion. Over the years, it is fairly predictable where each of us will go. No one ever sits in the front row. We teachers are the worst when it comes to sitting up front. I think maybe it stems from all those years in school where we were told it is best to sit up front to impress the teacher. Some folks choose to sit as a department in their "reserved" seats. The History Department seems to always do this even if it means unseating those new teachers who don't know where to sit. I find this mildly amusing. As for me, I always sit by the window near the back. This view of the meeting provides me the luxury of observing. I've learned so much by observing people over the years. As I settle into my seat, acknowledging those close to me with a smile, a nod, and a word, I quiet myself sipping my coffee and begin observing. I'm looking for the new teacher I will be mentoring.

Henry stands up and moves to the front of the library. I know I've said it before, but he is young. He is smiling and eager. It's hard not to like him. I think most everyone does, even if he's barely cut his teeth as an administrator. He begins to speak and I begin to listen.

He begins with a hearty Back to School pep talk about how glad he is that we are all there and how excited he is for the coming school year. He then moves into an explanation of our agenda items. Agendas were distributed as we entered by Janice Poulson, one of the all-time great administrative assistants. She always has a smile on her face, a bounce in her step, and is the central point person in the school for all things school-related. Not that she gossips . . . simply that she knows it all.

Today's agenda includes the typical introductions, a few announcements, and several discussion items. That will take us to lunch. Following lunch, we are to meet with our respective departments and spend time in our classrooms. This year, Henry has asked us all to rejoin together as a group at the end of the day for a new tradition, the Back to School first day send-off. We shall see what that's about. Rumor has it Henry attended a workshop this summer focusing on building team cohesion and morale. It appears that he will be trying out his new team building activities on us. I wish him luck with that. Seriously, I do.

The introductions begin. There are four new teachers starting today. It seems there are usually four new teachers starting every year. I wonder if that's typical. First we have Ms. Shoemaker, who appears to be a fairly mature woman of diminutive stature. She has recently moved to the area following her husband's transfer. She has been teaching for 22 years and will be joining the History Department. Once announced, I glance to the predictable gathering of the History Department and find her. It seems that she has already been welcomed and is comfortable with her new colleagues. A polite round of applause follows her introduction.

Next to be introduced is Sam Taylor. It is easy to find him in the crowd. He is the largest person in the room, and just finished playing college football. He will be joining the Physical Education and Health Department as well as the football staff as an assistant coach. He is greeted with a fairly raucous round of applause, whistles and hollering. Yes, our football program could use some young blood, and I'm sure most in the room are pinning their hopes on Sam to provide it. He grins widely in response and replies with a hearty, "Thank you so much! I'm so excited to be here! Go Mustangs!"

Following Sam's introduction is Carla. Carla is a new teacher in the Foreign Language Department. This is also her first year teaching. She speaks multiple languages and will be working specifically with our ESL program. I am reminded of when the only language spoken in school seemed to be English. It seemed like some of us even struggled with English at times. Spanish followed, and being bilingual became a real strength. Today, in our school alone, there are so many that I have lost track. But I am thankful that Carla will be here. We need teachers with her expertise who can bridge the gap for our students who aren't fluent in English. We applaud her presence.

Now, my ears are perked and I find myself sitting up and looking around intently. There's one more new teacher, and it dawns on me that this is the one that I will be mentoring.

Henry begins her introduction: "And finally, our last new teacher is Meghan Donahue. Meghan comes to us from Waco and will be joining the Language Arts Department."

She is slow to rise. As she stands, I am struck by her hair, the reddest hair I've ever seen. I don't know why this strikes me as funny, but it does. I've always been one to give nicknames to my colleagues, and Meghan will be no exception. Of course, hers will have to be "Ginger." This immediately makes me flash back to watching *Gilligan's Island* when I was a kid. What an absolutely far-fetched and ridiculous television show that was! And what a resounding success it was. Every one my age remembers *Gilligan's Island.* We had our own favorite characters that we related to. Mine was the Skipper. Once again, I digress.

I come back to the present moment. I am looking forward to meeting "Ginger." Maybe I will just stick with "Meg." We will see. I hope she has a sense of humor. I'm going to ask her to join me for lunch today.

The polite welcoming applause for Meghan subsides and we move on to the announcements. Henry picks up several papers and begins. I have to admit I have been known to tune out when announcements are being made. Year after year, some of the same things are said over and over. And here we go.

Henry begins with "Once again, this year our enrollment has increased, but our budget has remained the same. Therefore, please be mindful of the use of supplies and other materials and make every attempt to stick to your budgets."

Personally, I've never been one to really care about the budget and supplies or materials. I tend to not be attracted to shiny objects and, honestly, don't feel that having the best or newest supplies really has anything to do with whether or not students learn. Many of my colleagues disagree with me, and I can see the value of different teaching styles.

The second announcement is a bit more concerning. As all of us are woefully aware, there is increased concern about our school's safety and security. Henry explains that, although we don't want to believe it, we are not immune from the potential for violence. The horrible and tragic shooting of innocent children, teachers, and administrators has us all in a heightened state of concern. Yes, yes. I agree. To combat this concern and address the fears of parents, the decision has been made by the district to install security cameras both inside and outside of the building.

Whispered conversations break out among us for a few moments as Henry tries to explain more about it. He reminds us that Delmar is well behind, as most other schools around the country installed cameras years ago. It is now clear that most of us would like the opportunity to discuss this, and Henry decides, due to time constraints, that this will be addressed more during our next faculty meeting. For now, though, he simply wants us to be aware that cameras will be up and recording everything . . . the good, the bad, the ugly. He encourages us to share these concerns with our students. This includes things like picking your nose while standing at your locker, making out with your girlfriend in a back hallway, and bullying other students. Wow, am I thankful that they didn't have cameras in my high school when I was 16 years old. I shiver to think of what they may have captured me doing along with the knuckleheads that I hung out with! However, it's also amazing how people struggle with change. This is obviously good for all of us, and everyone will have to move past their concerns about the change.

We move on to the third and final announcement. I am feeling the effects of that huge, carb-loaded blueberry muffin and find myself completely drifting off into sugar low land when Henry says loudly, "And here's to our own Nathaniel Speer! As you all know, Shake was selected as the Texas High School Teacher of the Year. This is the first time we are all together since he accepted this award in July at a ceremony given in his honor in Austin. We are so proud of Nathaniel and happy that we can call him one of our own! Every one of us, but specifically you newer teachers can benefit from knowing Nathaniel. I encourage you all to get to know him better. Congratulations, Nathaniel!"

With that, all eyes turn around to find me. I can feel the blood rushing to my face and my heartbeat speeding up.

Meghan

Oh my goodness. There he is! In my mind, he has been larger than life ever since Principal Rodriguez told me last week that Nathaniel Speer would be my mentor this year. I hadn't heard of him before, so as soon as I could, I "Googled" him. Links to several articles about him came up right away. My new mentor had just won the most prestigious award for teaching in all of Texas! I felt so proud and so excited that he would be my mentor. I've already thought of things I want to ask him about so that I can get off to a good start in my teaching career.

I have high expectations of myself as a teacher, and since he clearly must also have had high expectations of himself, we will be a good match. My parents and teachers instilled the importance of high expectations in me at a young age, and I want to instill this into my students as well. Having Nathaniel as my mentor can only help me do this better than I had planned. I wonder if I'll ever feel comfortable enough to call him "Shake" like everyone else. I hope so.

As everyone stands to applaud him, I join them and turn around to see him for the first time. I realize that he is actually not larger than life. He is a rather average-looking, slightly balding older man. Not tall or small, not fat or thin, just all around rather average. Why didn't I do a "Google Image" search to see what he looked like? I don't know what I expected. Yes, actually I do know. As soon as I learned that he was the State Teacher of the Year, I imagined that he would be tall, striking in appearance, powerful in body language, and speak with a big Texas drawl. What I see now is this rather average man whose face is slowly turning red as he rises to acknowledge our standing ovation and applause.

He smiles broadly and raises his hands motioning for us to sit down. As I do, I notice his eyes for the first time. They appear to be blue, and I realize that he is smiling with his eyes. There is a mischievous glint in his eyes that is contagious.

He simply says, "Thank you all so much. I'm humbled to have received this award and am looking forward to this new school year. Let me know if I can help any of you in any way. That includes you too, Henry. I may not want to be an administrator, but as you all know, I've got certain strong opinions about how they should be running this ship!"

With that, the whole room cracks up laughing. I find myself laughing too even though I don't get this inside joke. I am laughing because this average-looking older man with the smiling eyes has absolutely no Texas drawl. In fact, it's some accent that I can't quite place. Maybe East coast, but not like my Boston cousins either. Hmmm, I'm further intrigued and can't wait to actually get to know this rather average guy with the smiling eyes and the mysterious accent. I already think I like this version of my mentor better than the larger than life version I had created. I feel my excitement growing even more.

Nathaniel

Well, as Back to School staff meetings go, this one has been pretty good. Once we got past the announcements and introductions, it was business as usual. The regular parade of suits stopped by to welcome all of us back. It seemed like everyone from the President of the PTA to the Chair of the Board of Education made an appearance.

The bulk of our remaining time was devoted to walking through our school calendar. This little exercise serves as a reminder of all of the required events such as holidays and student test days as well as extracurricular activities like sporting events, dances, Homecoming Week, and Prom. You know, there is a certain rhythm to the school year. There is a predictability that goes beyond seasons. I've always loved that rhythm. Although I am sure that one day I will retire, I'm not sure if that predictable rhythm of school will ever leave me. Who knows? Maybe I'll be one of those who, rather than fading into retirement, takes on the roles of tutoring, coaching, and even substitute teaching. It's never been clearer to me than it has become in the last several months that teaching is not something I do. Teaching is who I am.

Well, my thoughts have drifted again, and I am brought back to reality by two things. First, my stomach growls so loudly that Michael Riley of the History Department actually turns around, looks at me, pats his rather round stomach, and mouths "Let's eat!" I am slightly embarrassed. I realize that I am, indeed, quite hungry. It seems like it has been hours since the huge muffin this morning. I also notice that others are getting a bit squirmy too. I think this has as much to do with not having a bathroom break this morning as anything. I glance at my watch. It is 11:47 A.M. Thirteen minutes until we break for lunch. I know there is no way that Henry will excuse us for lunch even a few minutes early. He is a stickler for the agenda. Geez, I sound like one of those kids in my class who starts packing up their belongings while we are still engaged in the class. Those kids can really annoy me, but right now, I feel just like one of them.

OK, there it is. He thanks us for a great start to the day and excuses us for lunch, reminding us that the afternoon is to be spent in departmental meetings and in our classrooms. He concludes by reminding us, "Don't forget that we will meet back here again at the end of the day for a rousing sendoff!" That should be interesting.

Since I'd already decided to introduce myself to Ginger—er, Meghan—and see if she would like to have lunch with me, I begin sorting through the sea of teacher humanity to find her. There she is, surrounded by several other teachers all welcoming her and shaking her hand before they dash out the door and get on with their lunch plans. As I make my way across the room toward Meghan, who is now standing completely alone and appears to be a bit lost, I feel someone grab my elbow. I turn around quickly and there is my Language Arts Department Chair, Liz Rogers, holding onto my arm. I say, hey Liz, "How are you?"

"Oh, I'm doing well, Nate."

I actually prefer she not call me Nate. I wonder if she would be okay if I called her Lizzy.

"I just wanted to remind you that our department meeting will be in my room starting at 1:00 P.M. Don't be late!"

"Okay, okay, of course, I'll be there. Wouldn't miss it."

I turn around once more and now can't find her. *Where did she go? Is she gone?* I start walking faster toward the door thinking, "If Liz hadn't sidelined me . . ." Then I realize that I need to calm down. It's funny how such a little thing as this can get under my skin at times. I shouldn't let that bother me, but I struggle with her at times. An important lesson that I know I will impress upon Meghan is how to get along with people that you really just don't seem to get along with. Sometimes, we just have to agree to disagree. Sometimes, we just have to ignore. Sometimes, we just have to try to be the better person. I'm not feeling much like the better person right now and probably shouldn't have been so short with Liz. Well, that's a lesson for another day and another time.

I seem to have progressed from hungry to *hangry*. I think that word hangry is a great word. All English teachers love words. And hangry is a perfect word . . . hungry and angry!

One of my students used that word several years ago. She seemed to be having a bad day, and I asked her what was wrong.

She replied, "Nothing! I'm just really hangry!" She then proceeded to explain its meaning, and I've been using that word ever since.

Yes, I am hangry. I just need food and I need to find Meghan.

As soon as I exit the library door into the hallway, there she is. In fact, I almost run right into her as she is dashing back into the library.

"Oh excuse me," she says. "I'm so sorry. I seem to have forgotten my bag. I think I left it in the meeting. Oh, hi. I'm Meghan, one of the new teachers. And, well, congratulations on your award and well, I've been looking forward to meeting you. I understand that we are going to be working together. Well, of course we will be working together. You know, I am in the English department too. But, oh, I'm rambling. Sorry. Oh where was I sitting? I don't see my bag. Oh I'm sorry. Are you OK?"

At that, she has stopped talking and stops looking for her bag and is just staring at my face. I'm grinning from ear to ear. Not only does she have the reddest hair I've ever seen, but she is the fastest talker I have ever heard. It must have only taken her about five seconds to say all of it. So I say, "Yes . . . I'm just fine. Let's find your bag and grab some lunch. What do you say?"

"OK," she replies.

Meghan

Oh. My. Goodness. What is wrong with me? My excitement for meeting Nathaniel has turned to absolute embarrassment. Not only have I literally run right into him in the doorway but I have just now verbally vomited all over him! Settle down. He has just smiled very kindly and invited me to lunch. Settle down. Oh, there's my bag. OK, let's go to lunch. My excitement returns.

Nathaniel

As every teacher at our school knows, the options are limited around here for places to eat lunch. Unless you have taken the time to make and pack your own lunch (I don't think so), our options include the cafeteria, which usually isn't too bad. I love the lunch ladies, but it's not open yet since school hasn't started. This along with a few other local eating establishments is about it for a fast meal.

My favorite place for a great meal is easily Murphy's Market. No doubt about it. Just the thought of that place makes my mouth water. Although it's a real dive, it's the best Texas barbecue, ribs, and brisket place I've ever known. It's one of those places that you smell before you actually see it around the corner. I love that it is close to school and I can get in and out over a short lunch break. Just thinking of that place makes me want to go there right now. But, I doubt it is a place Meghan wants to go on her first day. I think I'll save that one for another time.

So where else could we go? Well there is also Red Fish Bar & Grill, Diego's Taqueria, and Nell's Cafe all within a ten-minute drive. If we hop in the car, we could easily get to the mall in about five minutes and eat at the food court. I know what we'll do. I hadn't been thinking sit-down restaurant since I usually don't have a whole hour for lunch. Today we do. So let's sit down.

I suggest that we jump in my truck and head to Nell's Cafe because they have a great salad bar. It's usually fast, the food is always good, and it will give us a chance to not rush. And, while not as exciting for me as Murphy's Market, Meghan might appreciate the salad bar option. So, Nell's Cafe, it is!

Meghan

Nathaniel says we are going to Nell's Cafe for lunch. I have no idea where that is. I've only just moved here and haven't given myself much of a chance to get to know the lay of the land.

Nathaniel just said, "I'll drive. It's not far."

It's dawning on me that we are going to get in his truck and drive to our lunch. I'm not sure what to think about this, but he seems to be in charge so I follow him.

As we approach what must be his truck, he apologizes for the mess that is going to be inside. He unlocks the doors and I open the passenger side as he opens the driver's side. And there is a bit of a mess in there. He begins to move papers and a book off of the passenger seat, putting them on the floor between us. There's a jacket and other clothes on my side also. He scoops them up and places them on the console between us.

"OK . . . get in."

I notice two coffee mugs in the cup holders and several used coffee cups on the floor. Apparently, he's a coffee drinker. For some reason, I am very glad that I know this about him. While his taste in coffee probably differs from mine, I find it rather comforting to know that he drinks coffee. And we're off.

Nathaniel

The drive to Nell's took all of eight minutes. Although Meghan was rather quiet on the way over, she was nonetheless polite as I asked her rather general questions: "Do you have a place to live?" "What did you think of this morning?" As we enter the restaurant, I glance around and see that several other teachers had the same idea as we did. Yes, getting to eat lunch away from school is a treat!

There is a group of four in line in front of us, and as we wait, I hear an energetic voice say, "Hey there, Shake! How are you?"

Meghan and I both turn to see that one of my former students, Raymond Espinoza, has entered behind us. Just seeing Raymond makes me smile. Shaking hands, he gives me a hearty pat on the arm and then a big hug.

I'm smiling, "Nice to see you, Raymond. Please meet Meghan Donahue, a new teacher in the Language Arts Department."

Grinning widely, Raymond responds, "Nice to meet you, Ms. Donahue."

Meghan replies, "Likewise."

Continuing, I ask, "What are you up to?"

Raymond chuckles and shares that he's just come from the hospital where his wife delivered their third child. He's stopped by to get some takeout for her as they celebrate.

I marvel at this, remembering when about fifteen years ago, Raymond sat in my class and hit on almost every girl in school. His hilarious sense of humor along with being an all-around great kid made it apparently almost impossible for the girls to resist. I worried about him and women until I received an invitation to attend his wedding. He'd gone on to graduate from college, had gotten a good job, and met the love of his life. Although I hadn't seen him in six years, he'd invited me to his wedding. Ginny and I attended, and it was wonderful.

And here he is again, randomly allowing me to be a part of another celebration in his life.

Wow, how time flies.

The hostess tells us to follow her. Raymond gives me another hug and says, "See you around, Shake!" and laughs.

I congratulate him on his new son, and Meghan and I take off after the hostess. As we walk away, I hear Raymond tell Meghan, "He's the best teacher I ever had. Pay attention to everything he does and you will be just fine."

This makes me smile. It's funny how we never know how we will be remembered. It seems like it is almost by luck that we are remembered at all.

On the way to our table, we pass three of the more veteran—OK, older—members of the Math Department. Margaret Hunt, Mona Del Vechio, and Mary Sanchez, aka 3M, are so busy talking to each other that they scarcely notice us as we pass. The 3M are known for their gossiping about anyone and everything. A standing joke at times, they have their collective fingers on the school's pulse, and you can always count on them to be in the know. Actually, truth be told, I have sought out their wisdom on more than one occasion when I have been confused or concerned about another teacher.

We are seated with menus in hand. Almost immediately, the choreography of the servers begins. Our glasses are filled with water by the bus boy. Then the waitress approaches, welcomes us, and describes the soups of the day. Today's options include tomato rice, broccoli cheddar, and chicken tortilla. Hmmm . . . that sounds good. The waitress tells us that she will give us a moment, and before I realize it I blurt out, "No need. I'm ready."

Meghan pops her head up as she closes her menu and says, "Me, too!"

The waitress addresses Meghan, who says, "I'll have your chicken tortilla soup and salad bar please."

The waitress turns to me, and I say "Make that two of those, but please make mine broccoli cheddar. I'd also like a glass of sweet tea."

The waitress looks at Meghan and she responds, "I'm good with water."

As the waitress leaves, I am feeling rather smug about my healthy choice for lunch. My mouth was watering for Murphy's Market barbecue before we decided on Nell's. I was also feeling like having Nell's juicy double cheeseburger on the way here. However, after hearing Meghan's order, I thought I would join her. Here's to good health!

Meghan excuses herself to go wash her hands, and I am left sitting alone at the table. Although I had given a bit of thought to how I would handle mentoring Meghan, something is itching at me about it right now. I'm not sure what it is. Over the years, I've mentored more than my share of novice teachers in a very informal way. Typically, we discuss various issues that they may be experiencing. You know, the regular stuff like discipline, lesson plans, resources, and assessments. Oh, how everyone hates assessments. In the past I've always taken the role of "sage on the stage" and accepted that as being "Oh, Wise One."

But for some reason, I don't want to repeat what I've done in the past. Running into Raymond Espinoza has reminded me that we often take for granted the real impact we might make on others. Why not form a different kind of relationship with Meghan? Why not be the "guide on the side" as opposed to the "sage on the stage?" Why not come alongside her and have her learn lessons about teaching without me lecturing on how it all works? Is there any reason that I can't change how I've done it in the past? Is there any reason that I can't try something entirely new and novel with Meghan? My mind begins to race, creatively thinking of alternatives. I haven't felt this kind of excitement to try something new in being a mentor in a long time.

And hold on, I think I've got it. And here it is.

As she returns from the restroom and sits at the table, I am truly looking forward to seeing how this goes. The food arrives. We both nod in approval and begin to eat.

"Meghan? Do you know how I came to be your mentor?"

Meghan looks at me with a somewhat puzzled face and says, "Not really. I guess I just thought someone in the administration asked you to help me."

"Actually, receiving that award ignited a spark in me that I hadn't felt for a while. I've been a good teacher for a long time, but, to tell you the truth, I hadn't felt like I was truly excited about teaching for a while. Of course, my students didn't know that, as I always gave my best as much as possible to my students. But I felt it. I felt like I was starting to become very comfortable and maybe even a bit stale. But then, with this award, I realized what an impact I had made on Luis. It got me thinking. It got me excited." I take a sip of my sweet tea. "You know who Luis is, right?"

Taking a bite of bread, Meghan pauses and replies, "I haven't had the chance to meet him, but I know he is the former student who nominated you for the award. He obviously felt like you made a difference in his life."

"I realized that I wasn't finished becoming the teacher that I was meant to be. I realized that there was more for me to accomplish, and I realized that, truthfully, I didn't have much time left to do it in my career. Seeing Raymond Espinoza just now also reminded me of this. So, I thought, what better way to leave a legacy than to be able to mentor a new teacher? And, with any luck at all she will long outlast me in the profession and will continue the legacy to future teachers she may one day mentor. This stream of consciousness really ignited my spark into a flame and, as soon as I heard that we had hired you in the English Department, I knew I wanted to connect with you. I essentially asked Henry if I could mentor you during my acceptance speech. So, here we are. What do you think?"

Meghan

What do I think? WHAT DO I THINK???? I think this may be crazy. I think that I may be in over my head with this guy! I think his need to make one final impact on education by mentoring me may fill some need for him. But what about me? Isn't this mentoring gig supposed to be about me?

These thoughts flash through my mind for what must have been an awkward ten seconds and then I look up and see his face and I relax. In that moment, I realize that he truly cares to leave a lasting mark. I see that he cares about me. I see that he has become energized in talking about our new relationship and what we might be able to achieve together.

So, to answer his question I reply, "Nathaniel, I am humbled. I don't quite know what to say. I'm thankful that you want to work with me and I truly am excited to learn from someone who clearly has impacted the lives of so many. Thank you. So, how will this work? What do you expect of me?"

Nathaniel

When Meghan paused after I told her of how she came to be my mentee, I actually was a bit worried. It only lasted a few seconds, but during that time, I almost felt it might not work. What if she didn't want some old coot like me to be her mentor? Even though I know that I come across as a seasoned veteran with thick skin, I felt quite vulnerable during those seconds of silence.

But then as she looked at me and I saw her confusion and untold thoughts whirling in her head, I also knew this was not personal. I am reminded of how I felt during that first day of becoming a teacher, and what I feel for her is empathy. I have experienced this same uncertainty, fear, and trepidation before.

And so now that she is on board and smiling, she asks, "How will this work? What do you expect of me?"

"OK, let's see. First of all, it's okay if you call me Shake like everyone else. Luis was the first student to call me that, and I didn't know what to think at first. But I knew he was coming from a good place when he started it. It caught on pretty quickly and now that is how most people at school refer to me. The older students and all of the teachers, custodial staff, kitchen workers, grounds keepers, and even the superintendent call me Shake. Nathaniel is perfectly fine as well. Whatever you feel comfortable with. I had a couple of nicknames in mind for you, but I'll go with Meghan if you are good with that."

Meghan pauses for a moment and says, "Let me guess, you were going to call me Rookie, Ginger, or Red? My friends growing up always called me Red."

"Actually, Ginger did cross my mind. It's probably best for us to use Mr. Speer and Miss Donahue whenever we are around the younger students. The upperclassmen are the ones who call me Shake, and it will be good for them to refer to you as Miss Donahue."

Both of our plates are empty, and I ask Meghan if she's up for seconds.

"No," she replies, "I think I'm good."

I laugh and say, "I'm definitely going back for more. How about more bread?"

She smiles. "No thanks. You have at it."

As I come back with my plate piled high, I say to Meghan, "It may take us a little while to figure out exactly how this will work. Sometimes the beginning of the school year can be hectic and you may find this particularly so as you establish a rhythm and routine to your new career and the day to day of teaching."

Meghan responds, "School hasn't even officially started and I already feel overwhelmed. I hope the rhythm and routine you mention will happen before too long."

"I assure you it will get better. I would say all new teachers are experiencing these same feelings at this point. As I see it, I think we will have both formal and informal meetings. Informally, we can talk daily about all of the logistical stuff that comes up. I want you to always feel free to ask if you have a question. Other teachers will be more than happy to help you as well. I've already checked your teaching schedule, and we both have the same planning period. Although on most days, you will be planning your own classes and I will be planning mine, it may be good for us to touch base a couple times a week to see how everything is going. Because I've been in your shoes, I know that you will have questions about some of your lessons."

Meghan takes another drink of her water as if to make a significant point. "I have so many questions, it's not even funny."

I chuckle and continue, "Sometimes, novice teachers are reluctant to share their first lessons for fear they aren't good enough. But, Meghan, I want to encourage you to bounce your ideas off of me and let me see your plans and pick your brain too. This will go both ways. You see, I, being an old geezer, know that I could benefit from your younger, more media-savvy insights. I would love the opportunity to see what you can teach me that might make my lessons a bit more relevant to today's kids. Frankly, it would shock my students, especially my seniors who I have taught in previous years, if I could integrate some cutting-edge technologies into my lessons. So, you see, these informal meetings will be good for both of us."

By now, Meghan is laughing. Her generation has never known life without technology. They have never known what a "real" telephone is or what it did. I, on the other hand, still fumble and bumble around on my "smart" phone. While I watch others text with just one thumb, I stumble around the keys with fingers like stuffed sausages. Thankfully, there is autocorrect or I'd be sunk.

We chat about this for a minute more, and then Meghan says, "Nathaniel, having the informal meetings will really help me, I'm sure. You know, I did fairly well in all of my college teaching method classes, but I was only taught 'one right way' to write a lesson plan. And, although I did that well, I have known in the back of my mind that I would need to be much more creative. I just didn't know where to start. Now I feel comfortable coming to you and starting with you. Thank you."

"You're very welcome," I reply.

As I'm explaining these logistics, Meghan is nodding and smiling. Her energy is increasing as she replies, "That sounds great."

"I was thinking we could also meet once a month or so for a longer, more formal meeting. There we can talk about what you can expect in a career as a teacher, and maybe I can share some of the lessons I've learned in my journey. When I say formal, I just mean that we will have a designated time and place to meet. We can figure out the logistics of the meetings at a later time.

"I think these should be conversations. Perhaps, conversations that begin with a question. One of the hardest things for novices to learn is to take the focus off of themselves and just start observing. So this is what I want you to begin to do. Obviously, for our informal meetings, the focus will be on you and on me and how we can mutually help each other with our lessons including objectives, content, delivery, assessment, etc. It's the meat of the day-to-day, so to speak.

"For our conversations during those more formal meetings, I want you to start observing. What do you see? What do you hear? What do you sense? What do you feel? What is becoming made known to you? We can call these 'Noticings and Wonderings.' I want you to observe thoughtfully, listen for clarity, and acknowledge what you feel. This is the beginning of becoming a reflective practitioner. I encourage you to keep a daily journal of these observations. At the end of the day, take a few moments to reflect on what you saw or heard or felt and then ask yourself, what did I learn? What did I learn about what I saw or heard or felt? What did I learn about the context? What did I learn about the educational process from it? And, most importantly, what did I learn about myself as I am becoming a teacher?"

Meghan has taken out a small notepad from her bag and is now taking notes. This makes me smile. I think I'm going to really like this. I then signal for the waitress that we would like the check. Suzy always laughs when I signal for the check. I think holding my hand in the air and acting like I am writing is a great way to ask for the check. But, now that I think about it, many of them ask me if I am ready to pay the bill when they see me make that motion. That might mean the signal isn't the universal sign for needing to pay. Our waitress comes to the table and asks if we are ready for the check.

"And one last thing, Meghan. This one isn't necessarily easy. You will observe situations that you do not agree with. It might be what a teacher is doing, or how a student is behaving. It might be how a student is dressed or the language he or she is using. It might be in something an administrator says or how students are interacting. It might be a myriad of things that you will experience and observe that you will not like and you will not agree with. This will trigger feelings and emotions in you that you may not like either. But—and I want to emphasize the BUT—I want to urge you to 'remove the judgment hat.' I am sure you already know it, but we all have our own biases and prejudices that come from our own learned experiences. I had a hard time believing this about myself. Just be aware and make note of it. These observations, emotions, and reflections will also cause you to create questions about what you are experiencing, seeing, feeling, and thinking. So, bring your questions to our formal meetings. If you've done your homework well, these questions will be good ones. Challenge me with your questions and let's see what we can both learn."

Meghan puts down her pen and gives me a look of excitement mixed with skepticism. As the waitress refills my iced tea and her water, Meghan replies, "I'm really looking forward to seeing how this goes."

"Enough of the wisdom for today. Let's just get to know one another."

CHAPTER 4

The Backstory

Meghan

"Tell me about you," Nathaniel asks. "Where are you from? What about your family? How did you arrive at Delmar High School?"

"I've always enjoyed telling people the story of how and where I grew up," I begin, taking a long sip of water.

It's been an interesting journey for sure. My dad was a career military guy and was stationed in San Antonio when my two brothers and I were born. I am the oldest. Mike is two years younger than me and Chris is two years younger than him. I don't remember much about San Antonio because we left there when I was six years old and my dad retired after 25 years of service.

One of his assignments in the Air Force was in a very remote section of Alaska. He was stationed there on two different occasions and told my mom that he wanted to take his family to live there some day. Believe it or not, my parents sold everything they had and bought a thirty-foot Holiday Rambler travel trailer that we were to live in until we could find a permanent place in Alaska. They bought a four-door pickup truck to pull the trailer, and we set out for Alaska. To provide perspective, it is about 4,000 miles from Texas to Anchorage, Alaska. You can drive from San Antonio to Great Falls, Montana and you aren't quite halfway to Anchorage. What an adventure! It took us two solid weeks to get to Anchorage. We traveled through Alberta, British Columbia and the Yukon Territory, fishing, hiking, and taking in the spectacular scenery.

My dad got a job working for the state of Alaska, and we moved to a remote village 50 miles from the nearest town. We had a one-room school building in our little village for 1st–6th grades. There was a husband and wife team that taught us. Mrs. Finley taught 1st–3rd grades and her husband Mr. Finley taught 4th–6th grades. I can truly say that is where my love for learning and teaching was born. Both of them were incredible teachers. They had such a passion for kids. They worked very hard to get to know each of us as individual learners. Granted, it might have been easier than most teachers have it because I never had more than three other kids in my grade. Regardless, they made learning fun, and I remember thinking I wanted to be like them.

I've always loved school and eagerly awaited the first day of school each year with anticipation and excitement. Several of my family members were teachers, and when I was in high school, I loved watching them get ready to go back to school each year. Sometimes, they would even let me come into their classrooms before the school year started and help them get organized and decorate it to welcome back their students.

But it was in the fourth grade that I really made the decision that I, too, was going to become a teacher. That was the year that I first had Mr. Finley for a teacher. Don't get me wrong, Mrs. Finley was a great teacher, and I learned so much from her. But what I learned from Mr. Finley changed my life.

This man with the Midwest accent and the infectious sense of humor who had been teaching for years made me realize that learning was fun and that I was fully capable of learning anything and everything he taught. And more than anything, Mr. Finley taught me that I was lovable and that he cared about me. He didn't just care about what I learned. He sincerely cared about me as a ten-year-old. And not just me, he cared about all of his students the same way. If he had favorites, we never knew it. He wanted to know about our lives, our pets, our friends, our families, our interests, our strengths, and our challenges. Mr. Finley was there for all of us, all the time. From Mr. Finley, I learned that teachers could and should genuinely care about their students. He was unapologetic about loving us. And because he loved us, he held us to high and uncompromising standards of excellence as students in his classroom. Mr. Finley was the first teacher I had who truly saw the gifts that I had that no one else had seen or recognized before.

He gave me my first teaching job when he asked me to skip recess to help another student, Patrick, who was struggling to read. He referred to me as his teacher, and day after day, rather than play on the playground those few months, I sat with Patrick alone in the classroom, and taught him to read. So it was thanks to Mr. Finley that I decided to become a teacher.

With the decision made, I began to behave as if I was a teacher. I played school with my friends, organizing my bedroom into my own classroom. I asked for a portable blackboard for Christmas so I could write on the board as I taught. Sometimes, I played school with friends or my brothers, but many times, I played it alone. I organized books into a small library and I took my parents' National Geographic magazines after they were finished with them. The maps from inside those magazines began to adorn the walls of my bedroom, ready for when I would teach geography. I wrote out a welcoming talk and practiced it aloud so that I would be ready for my students when I became a teacher. I voraciously read everything I could get my hands on and used what I learned reading to create lessons with stories for my students.

As the years progressed from 4th grade through high school, I realized that I was constantly focused on what teachers did, what they said, and who they were. I realized that I was becoming a teacher before actually being a teacher. I took advantage of every opportunity to speak up and help others when they had questions. I wanted to be the one that other students turned to when they didn't understand or have the answers. I loved school so much and wanted to be a teacher so much, that I was sure that nothing would get in the way of my becoming a teacher.

Nathaniel looks at me as if he is amazed and says, "You were so fortunate to have those two teachers in such formative years of your life. I think I'm a little envious."

I smile as I take another long sip of water. Then I continue my story.

There were other ways Mr. Finley would make learning more meaningful. For example, he would take the 4th–6th graders outside in the winter and we would collect a square foot of snow and melt it to see how much water that produced. The people in the surrounding area came together and built an Olympic-size outdoor hockey rink, and he taught us about measurements as we helped cut, paint, and set in place the boards for the wall of the rink. We learned how much water it took to fill a hockey rink with three to four inches of ice.

But the learning opportunity I remember most involved salmon, a fish wheel, and a group of elderly Native Americans. Like many Native American villages, the one we lived next to was located on a river. The Copper River was less than half a mile behind our house. For the first couple of weeks in June each year, the salmon would begin arriving. Native Americans were allowed by the government to have a fish wheel that was mounted on the river bank. The fish wheel for our community was essentially two wire mesh baskets that rotated with the current on an axis. The fish swam into the baskets and then dropped into a trough on the side. I don't remember exactly how big the trough was, but I remember it being large enough to hold lots of salmon.

During this two-week period in June, we would walk down to the fish wheel twice a day alongside Mr. Finley in his tractor. We would meet the elderly members of the village and help them take the salmon from the trough to the bucket on the tractor and then walk along with the tractor to the village where we would unload the fish. There were days we would unload up to 50 King, Silver, and Pink salmon. In assembly line format, we helped clean the fish and listen to fascinating stories of the history of that region of Alaska. We learned how to filet salmon for steaks, hang the salmon in the smokehouse for smoked fish, and can the salmon for multiple uses. I will forever remember how much I enjoyed school and the life lessons I learned with the Finleys.

"Wow, what an incredible experience," Nathaniel interrupts me. "Do you like to fish? I ask because I love to fish, and it's one of the main reasons I moved down here. I can tell you more about that at some point. I just got a little excited, and my interest seems to go to a whole new level when I hear someone talk about fishing."

I laugh as I take another drink of water. "I actually do like to fish and spent many days on various streams, rivers, and lakes with my dad and brothers."

There's nothing like being on a river when the salmon are running. We also fished on a lake that was 25 miles into the woods. The only way you could access it was by four-wheeler or floatplane. Several people that lived close by had floatplanes and would take us back there a few times each year to fish for trout. It was incredible as well.

Back to my school experience. There was no middle school in our village. So, we traveled 50 miles each way every morning and afternoon for 7th and 8th grades. I was the last one to be picked up in the morning and the first one to be dropped off in the evening. Two girls lived 30 miles further up the road and traveled 80 miles round trip each day. In the winter, we would go to school in the dark and return home in the dark because the days were so short. The sun would rise around 9am and set about 3 PM. Conversely, we could play outside until midnight in the summer months with no lights because the sun set about 2am and rose again around 4am. I was a true tomboy during my time in Alaska, and I have such fond memories of that time in my life.

Once I finished 8th grade, my parents felt it was best if we moved back to Texas in hopes it would provide more opportunities. My high school years were pretty typical . . . sports, dances, boys, summer jobs, etc. I also continued my love for learning and tried to learn something about teaching from as many teachers as I could. Like anything, there were good teachers and bad ones, but I learned from each of them.

As you can imagine, I had no trouble identifying my major in college. I declared as an education major as soon as I could in my sophomore year. I had a great experience as a student teacher, and I applied for several teaching positions. However, this one was the only one outside the Dallas area that I even considered. I don't know what it was, but something intrigued me about teaching in South Texas and the opportunities and challenges that might present. So here I am!

Nathaniel

"What a great story you have," I say to Meghan. "You had an incredible childhood. I've always wanted to go to Alaska. Maybe I'll make that trip now that I have a connection with someone who knows the lay of the land. And I love that you like to fish. That is a great connection we already have. We will have to go fishing some time."

I notice the time; we will have to leave soon to get back to our departmental meeting. The restaurant is starting to clear out and I've noticed all of the teachers who were here when we arrived have left as well. I'm sure our waitress is ready for us to leave so she can finish her shift and go home, but I am enjoying this conversation. We will leave soon. I want to give Meghan a sense of how I got to this place as well.

"My story isn't quite as exciting as yours."

To tell you the truth, I'm not sure I ever really thought I could become a successful teacher. It is humbling to realize that you can really make a difference. In hindsight, though, I'd have to say that there were several times I wasn't sure I would survive the profession. As the old saying goes, "Teaching is a journey, not a destination." It has been an incredible journey for me through the years. I have learned so much about myself as a person and as someone who is trying to influence young people on a daily basis. Teaching requires you to be reflective. It requires you to be observant. I realized early on that I needed to watch and emulate what other teachers were doing. I had to understand what was working for them and what was not. And, I can tell you, I learned so much from those other teachers. And this required that I reflect on what I was doing compared to what they were doing. I had to take a critical look every day at my successes in the classroom and, more importantly, my challenges.

I grew up in the heart of Philadelphia and went to Delphine High School. I didn't necessarily love school from an early age. School was always important because my parents made sure it was a priority for me. However, I certainly didn't go out of my way to do extra work and think of myself as a teacher in elementary school.

Growing up in such a big sports town as Philadelphia, I was

convinced I was going to play center field for the Phillies or quarterback for the Eagles, and I spent any free time I had playing sports with my buddies. Once I got to high school, I began to realize those dreams were not likely to happen.

I've known since I was in tenth grade that I wanted to be a teacher. Mrs. Sedgewick was my Language Arts teacher, and she inspired me and most all of the other students in her classes because she cared enough to take a personal interest in each of us.

Janie Templeton broke my heart that fall, and we were in Mrs. Sedgewick's class together. It was very difficult for me to be in the same classroom with Janie. To make matters worse, we were in the same group together for a project assignment, and it must have been pretty apparent as Mrs. Sedgewick asked me to stay after class one day. She didn't want to pry too much into my private life. She simply said, "I can tell you are hurting and I am more than willing to move you to another group. I know there are a couple of students who wouldn't mind switching with you."

I said thanks and I would think about it. I didn't end up moving out of that group (partially because of my pride), but I remember thinking that my teacher cared, and I would like to help other kids if they were ever hurting in some way.

I also remember being aware of how passionate Mrs. Sedgewick was about whatever subject matter we were covering. She had this great ability to bring the content to life. We explored several short stories that year. One in particular that stood out for me was "The Monkey's Paw." It's a short story written by W. W. Jacobs with the characters Mr. and Mrs. White, their adult son Herbert, and a friend of Mr. White, Sergeant-Major Morris.

The plot of the story is that the owner of the monkey's paw is granted three wishes, but the wishes come with a price because the owner is interfering with fate. Mr. White takes possession of the monkey's paw and the story describes the subsequent tragedies that affect the family.

To help bring this story to life, Mrs. Sedgewick enlisted two other teachers and an administrative assistant, and the four of them played the characters and performed for the class. Each of the characters was in full costume, and we all felt like we were in England at the turn of the 20th century. She was constantly thinking of different ways to make the material interesting for us. I looked forward to her class each day.

Fast forward six years, and I was a student teacher at Greystone High School. My supervising teacher was Mr. Tremble. He was a veteran teacher and didn't seem at all thrilled to take on the duties of mentoring a student teacher. Actually, while not thrilled, I think he took me on so that I could do most of the work for him. That experience was the epitome of trial and error. He threw me into teaching right away without an opportunity to observe him. He said I had to learn at some point and that the best way to learn how to teach was to jump right in. I didn't have an opportunity to get to know the students and what they had learned. My lessons were a disaster, and to make matters worse, Tremble wasn't really available for me to talk with or ask for advice.

I couldn't wait to be finished with that experience. I had such high hopes for how it was going to go that spring. I went into student teaching convinced that I was going to change the world, and I left it questioning whether I really wanted to become a teacher. I couldn't imagine a career where I might become a teacher like him. It was hard to imagine that he was always like that.

I graduated from college in May 1986, and I wanted to teach somewhere very different than where I grew up and went to school. I wanted to experience rural America, and I wanted to be somewhere close to the ocean. My best friend growing up and his family had a house on the South Jersey Shore, and they would often invite me to vacation with them for a week or two at a time. What a great time we had. The one activity I enjoyed the most was fishing with him and his dad. They had a boat, and we would take it into the open water at least a couple of times during each of my visits. We caught tons of fish and had lots of laughs. We also spent time on the boat closer to shore just hanging out and talking and philosophizing about every subject you can imagine. I also spent a good bit of my youth fishing with my dad and grandfather. I'll go into that later.

The one other criterion I had for my ideal job was that it would be somewhere warm. I love Philly and the Northeast, but I wanted to be on the water and not freezing my tail off five months out of the year. So, I applied to positions in Alabama, Texas, and Louisiana during that spring before I graduated. I didn't know anyone in any of those three places. Despite my mother's trepidation, I was adventurous and had the attitude that I could always move back home if it didn't work out for me.

I remember being a little panicked because it was late June and I didn't have a job yet. I was working for my uncle that summer as a painter. He was a contractor who had several crews painting houses. I worked for him all through high school in the summers and over winter breaks. I had resigned myself to the fact that I might have to work with him for a year and apply for teaching positions the following year. I didn't want to do that, but I was thinking it might be my only option.

Then I got a call from Susan Walliford, the principal here at Delmar. I had to look on a map to see where it was located. We talked for well over an hour, and then I had to interview with the head football coach, Jim Leavenworth. The position was Language Arts teacher, Student Council Sponsor and Assistant Freshman Football Coach. Jim was an intriguing guy to say the least. I had an interesting experience with him, but I don't want to get ahead of myself.

I must have done okay in the interview because Susan called me the next morning and offered me the position. I felt really good about the teaching position and being a sponsor of an organization. I had no experience as a football coach, but it was part of the position. I had a job, and I was moving to South Texas.

I didn't have much time, as I was supposed to be there the first week of August for new teacher orientation. What I didn't realize was that football practice started well before that. Actually, formal practice didn't start until August 1, but the weight room was open, and the kids were expected to participate in "voluntary" workouts. Coaches of the freshman team were expected to be there as well to supervise workouts. Even though I just accepted the position, I had to get here as soon as I could. Susan had given me the names of the two apartment complexes in town.

I filled a small U-Haul and towed my Honda Civic behind. After two 10-hour days of driving, I was so excited to be in Texas. Little did I know, I was still 500 miles from Delmar. Texas is huge! I arrived late on a Friday afternoon and must say I was surprised how remote my new home was compared to anything I'd ever known. I was wiped out and stayed that night at The Sand Dunes Motor Lodge. That place isn't even around anymore. I looked for apartments the next day and moved into a one-bedroom. I started right away monitoring football workouts and attending meetings. I had little time to prepare for my classes, but I managed to pull it together in time.

At the time, Delmar was a school of 500 students in grades 9–12. I quickly learned that Susan cared about her teachers and wanted me to succeed. I couldn't have asked for a better leader to help me make the transition from student to teacher. She taught English for fifteen years before moving into an administrative position. She "got it" when it came to what teachers deal with on a daily basis. She was very honest with me regarding the potential challenges I would face in my first year of teaching. Many of the kids were from single-parent homes. Seventy percent of the students were on free and reduced lunch, and parental involvement was practically non-existent. Not much has changed since then.

Susan was careful not to label any of the kids I would meet and teach because she didn't want me to have any pre-conceived notions about individual kids. That is something many teachers did that would drive Susan crazy. She felt it was unfair to the students if a teacher had a pre-conceived notion that might prevent the teacher from giving the student a chance. That is something I have always remembered and work very hard to avoid when talking to other teachers about students.

"I do have a story about a situation with a student I didn't handle very well," I say to Meghan as I ask for a glass of sweet tea to go. "It didn't go well, in part because I labeled this student without realizing it. Remind me to tell you about it when we talk about my struggles those first few years of teaching. Guess I better take care of this check so we can get going. I was going to give you a hard time and tell you that you had to pay. But, I couldn't bring myself to do that. This one's on me."

Meghan is very gracious and replies, "Thanks so much. I didn't expect you to do that."

I can tell she has more to say as I say, "You are more than welcome. My pleasure."

"I think it's great that you took such a chance and moved far away from home," Meghan says. "Obviously, it would have been easy for you to stay somewhere closer to family and friends. This must be a pretty special place for you to have stayed here for so long. I look forward to hearing more about what kept you here."

"Well, we are running short on time and need to get back to school in a few minutes. Before we go I'd like to try and capture some of my thinking about this process as we move forward. One of the things that I have learned over time in my educational career is that many teachers and administrators fail to describe the *why* to their constituents before proceeding to the *what* and the *how*. I used to think it was all about the latter two until I realized that people have a far greater likelihood of success when they understand the *why* before venturing into the implementation process. I believe you can benefit greatly from it as a student in this process, and I know your students will be the beneficiaries when you share the information as their teacher.

"My *why* for you is to become the type of teacher who helped motivate you to choose teaching for a career and the teacher who left a lasting impression on you as an individual. The one you want to go back and visit just to say thanks and let him or her know that you lived up to the faith that was expressed to you. I also want you to be able to move from novice to master teacher faster and more efficiently than I did in my career.

"As I've aged and especially since receiving this honor, I have reflected more and more on what it takes to be a great teacher. In my case it was a great deal of trial and error, failing forward and failing fast. Looking back now I also realize that I remained positive, optimistic, persistent, and resilient most of the time as well. In hindsight, that helped me immeasurably. I always knew I wanted to be a teacher, so professional investment and commitment was never an issue for me. Unfortunately, we lose many new teachers early in their careers because they get discouraged, lose hope, and don't receive the type of mentoring and support necessary to survive the initial stages of their teaching careers. This is another *why* for me. I want you to feel like you are not alone and to build your stamina and confidence so you can weather some storms without sinking.

"I've heard the field of teaching described by some educational experts as a 'profession without a practice.' I believe their intent was to say that unlike many other professions, teaching does not necessarily have a set protocol or specific guidelines which all practitioners must adhere to. Instead, there are a variety of strategies, practices and approaches which can be employed to achieve success. You know what that sounds like to me? Fishing! Lots of techniques, equipment, styles and strategies available to anglers to pursue their species of choice.

"I think fishing and teaching have so much in common. There is certainly no shortage of theories, articles, empirical studies, wives tales, theses, and research on both topics. You could become overwhelmed attempting to sort through everything. Over the years I have realized that most teachers are like the fishermen I know. They love to collect things like lesson plans, tests, lures, baits, etc. Sometimes it can seem like an episode of Hoarders when you see what some teachers and fishermen collect because you just never know when it may come in handy. I want you to be knowledgeable and comfortable going 'old school' or 'new school.' I want you to respect and understand the past while also being excited about the future.

"I must admit that my head starts to spin a bit when I think about how to best go about this process. I feel that I have something to offer you, but when I listen to you share your background I realize that you have much to offer me as well. I want you to know that I'm not interested in making you in my own image as a teacher or living vicariously through your life. I am interested in seeing if I can share with you my observations over the years so that your journey will be productive, fulfilling and enjoyable. You know, that is where this process may be different than fishing."

"How is it different?" Meghan asks me.

"I'm not sure if you experienced this in your family growing up, but I certainly did in mine. When I was little and before I started fishing with my buddy and his dad off the Jersey Shore, there were a couple of other people I got to fish with pretty regularly. This was at the lake where my grandparents had a small cottage. My dad spent his childhood summers there. My dad, my grandpa and I used to hammer those perch and largemouth bass. I mean 40–50 fish that were just monsters every time we went out.

"Looking back now it seemed like it was some covert CIA operation if you weren't part of Poppy's trusted fishing network. He would be paranoid about outsiders discovering our best spots or the bait the fish were hitting on. I remember him telling me not to set my hook so high in case others were watching or if someone came by and asked, 'Are they biting?' My dad and I were under strict instructions to respond 'not so much' or 'pretty slow' unless Poppy gave the green light by talking first. Heck, there were even times when we had fish on the line and he wouldn't let us reel them in until the coast was clear of strangers.

"On the other hand, though, if you were one of his friends he would be more than happy to give you the depth, location based on cottage and tree markings, and every bait that had worked for the last month. I'm not the type to keep secrets when it comes to fishing or teaching. Catching fish is fun; the same is true for capturing the hearts and minds of students. I may not have all the answers, but I certainly am willing to share any knowledge that I have begged for, borrowed, or stolen over the years. You up for that?"

"I'm in!" Meghan replies.

"Awesome. It's going to be a great year. We need to get back though. Your new department chair doesn't like it when we are late. You also need to know these next several days of orientation are going to be very helpful for you."

As we drive back to the school, I keep thinking about the similarities between teaching and fishing. "What do you think about fishing during our monthly meetings?" I ask Meghan. "I have a boat we could use. We could meet at the marina boat ramp and spend a Saturday morning once a month fishing the Laguna Madre. Sound good?"

Without hesitation, Meghan says, "Wow, that would be awesome! I've heard great things about how good the fishing is there. I haven't done much fishing at all since I lived in Alaska, so I might be a little off my game. But just let me know when and where. I'll be there."

"Great," I reply. Let's plan on the first Saturday in September for our initial fishing trip to discuss your first few weeks of school."

We pull into the school parking lot, and I'm excited about the potential for helping this newbie navigate her teaching journey.

CHAPTER 5

Reality Sets In

Meghan

Teaching: Day 1

Why didn't anyone tell me about the traffic? How could I not know that traffic on the first day of school would be this bad? Where did all these people come from? Is it always like this? I'm going to be late! Well, not late exactly. Obviously I will be there in time for the bell to ring for classes to begin. But, I really wanted to get to my classroom with about an hour of time to just get "ready." Ready for what, I'm not sure.

I guess the feedback I've gotten so far suggests that I'm ready. My classroom is set up, my bulletin boards are decorated, and my lesson plan for each class is complete. I went to bed early last night to make sure I'd be well-rested. I woke up before my alarm, took a shower, had my tea and banana, and put on my good luck blouse.

That was a bit of a struggle. Trying to decide what to wear today has been a three-day process. I must have tried on a dozen different outfits. What does it mean to dress like a teacher anyway? So many choices. Skirt or pants, sweater or jacket, sleeveless or sleeves, heels or flats, shirt tucked or not, bare legs or tights. What about colors? I didn't want to be too "matchy-matchy" but I also didn't want to appear too nonchalant in my clothing choices. Why was I so worried about this?

Well, I know why. I am trying to impress. Yes, dress to impress. But who am I dressing to impress?

Of course, I need to impress my students. I need them to believe that I am a professional teacher, that I am competent, and that I won't tolerate any monkey business. After all, I am only a few years older than the seniors and eight years older than my youngest 9th graders. And obviously, I want to impress the other teachers, but more than that I want to fit in and not stand out with regard to my wardrobe. Why didn't I ask one of them what they wear on the first day?

The person I really should have asked is Nathaniel. He would have known exactly what I should wear. What a help he's been these last few days as everyone is gearing up for the first day of school! And now it dawns on me. The person that I am really trying to impress as a professional is Nathaniel. Of course, he's my mentor now. I hope my wardrobe choice for today is professional and appropriate . . . button-down light blue and white stripe tailored shirt, navy slacks, light blue sweater, small heels, small hoop earrings, and a new watch. I also have pulled my hair back into a low teacher-like ponytail. I think I look very professional.

I am especially pleased with the watch. I've never even owned a watch. Actually, none of my peers own a watch. We all tell time with our phone. When Nathaniel noticed this, he just laughed and shook his head muttering something about millennials under his breath. I also laughed and then told my mom about it.

Two days later, the UPS man left an Amazon Prime box on my doorstep. Upon opening it, there was a beautiful new watch from Mom. Her note read, "For my daughter, the teacher. May you always be on time. Love, Mom xxxooo."

Over the course of my musing, I hadn't noticed that I had been making slow but steady progress toward school. As I now park and walk into the building, I feel the excitement escalating along with some nerves. My pace quickens as I greet several other teachers and watch them scurry off to their classrooms. It's time to scurry off to mine. Let's do this!

It is still quiet as I sit at my desk observing my classroom. I've had about 30 minutes to review my lessons and focus my thoughts.

Nathaniel just popped his head in, gave me a quick thumbs up, and said "Looking good. Are you ready?"

I almost replied, "Ready as I'll ever be." But then realized that I knew what I was really ready for. "Yes, I'm ready. I'm ready to learn how to become a teacher."

"Then you are ready," he replied. "Today they will call you teacher." With that, and a big smile, he left.

I can hear the beginnings of the sounds of school. Homeroom is first. Footsteps, voices, laughter, locker doors slamming. I step outside of my classroom by the door and watch them. They are of every size, color, and shape. Some greet each other with fist bumps, nods, and hugs. Others walk down the hall seemingly appearing to hide as they duck and weave through the crowd. Still others seem to notice no one and proceed as if in their own bubble with earphones in and heads down. As I observe them, I am thankful. I am thankful that some of these will be my students. I am thankful that today I begin my career as a teacher. With that thought lingering, the bell suddenly rings. Here we go.

The bell again suddenly rings and they bolt from their seats and dash out the door. All I can do is watch them go. This pattern has presented itself all day. Bell rings, students in, bell rings, students out. Somewhere between students in and students out, I was a teacher. But I'm not sure I was any good. As they left, several said "See ya!" or "Bye." No one said "Thank you." I glance at the new watch and see that Day 1 is over. Now what?

I find that I am still standing at the front of the class and move to walk to the door and glance into the hall. Students are dispersing in different directions. Lockers are slamming once again. The noise level diminishes. I feel a bit shell shocked. Just then as I turn to go back into the classroom, I hear a now familiar voice.

"Well, how was your day?" Nathaniel asks.

"Is it over?" I reply.

"Yep . . . it's over. Let's walk down to the teachers' lounge for a few minutes. There's usually some food left on the first day, and I like to see how everyone else is doing today. OK?" And we walk.

Although it only takes about three minutes to get to the teachers' lounge, I immediately feel better when we enter. The mood in here is energetic as other teachers are grabbing a cookie and something to drink.

We enter and Nathaniel proudly announces, "Well, she made it! Remember your first day? She has made it through her first day! I think we should keep her."

There is much laughter and congratulations all around. I feel a bit embarrassed but break into a smile. What a great feeling. It gives me a sense of belonging to them, this place, this profession, and to being a teacher.

And yet, in the back of my mind, a small red flag is rising. Can I live up to their expectations? How long will it take before I actually finish my lesson plan? How long before I know the students' names? How long before I truly begin to own an identity as teacher? How long before I become as good a teacher as Nathaniel? More importantly, will I ever become a teacher as good as Nathaniel? Too much to think about. I politely excuse myself to return to my classroom. Time to get ready for tomorrow.

Teaching: Day 10

Nathaniel reminded me this morning that tomorrow is our first fishing trip. We're going to meet at Bill's Bait Shop across from the marina. I can't wait to go fly fishing again.

I could fill a journal with everything that I didn't know over the past nine days. Here I am, two weeks into my teaching career, and I have already let myself down. Before starting, I laid out some fairly simple (at least I thought they were simple) personal goals. I looked at them like learning targets. At the end of the day, I can check them off and feel a sense of accomplishment.

Personal Goals:

1. Decide on clothes before going to bed.
2. Prepare and pack my lunch before going to bed.
3. Work out 3–4 times each week.
4. Write in journal every day before going to bed.
5. No work on Sunday.

How hard could that be? I mean, I've always been organized and had excellent time management skills. But in only two short weeks, I have managed to break every one of these goals. It feels like these were more like New Year's resolutions that are broken within a few weeks rather than personal improvement goals.

The clothes situation has me spinning. I have realized that most of my wardrobe is more appropriate for college sorority girl life and inappropriate for teaching. However, my beginning teacher salary will only stretch so far. I guess less Netflix and Starbucks, and more Target.

My nutritional situation is also more complex than I imagined it would be. I don't know why I thought that I would just eat cafeteria food. It's fast, it's easy, but really? I know they say it is nutritionally sound, but I simply cannot bring myself to eat it every day. Nathaniel loves it. I think he loves it because it means his wife won't make his lunch. Apparently, she wants him to be healthier, but he seems to think that means eating cardboard.

The first four days of school flew by so fast that I didn't even eat lunch at all. My half hour scheduled lunchtime was spent trying to switch gears from teaching my third English 9 class to English 11, which I'm now co-teaching with Nathaniel. I have three English 9 classes in a row, all with the same lesson plan. However, the third one, which I thought would be the easiest one since I'd already had the same lesson twice before, has become more of a challenge. It's an inclusion class.

Although all of the students in the class are 9th graders, five kids have special needs. This requires and allows a Special Education teacher to accompany them and assist in the class. Although I should welcome the help, I would prefer to "sink or swim" on my own rather than have an experienced Special Education teacher observing me. Well, she's not really observing ME, and she has been helpful. But, I'm just not sure of myself enough to feel comfortable with her in the room every day. I'm not even sure what all of the needs are for these students.

Although lunch is right after this, it is only 30 minutes long. By the time I decompress from the inclusion English 9 class, go to the bathroom (finally!) and then prepare to co-teach with Nathaniel in English 11, lunch is over. And I missed it.

So after the first four days of missing lunch, I tested out the Friday lunch options at the cafeteria. Big mistake! Not only were there poor choices nutritionally, I had to grab and go. I inhaled my lunch, ran back to the classroom, and suffered indigestion for the rest of the day. I came home that night and added that second goal over the weekend.

This week, I managed to prepare and pack a healthy, well-rounded lunch before going to bed exactly twice. I threw together some granola bars and a protein shake one day while running out the door. And today, I went without.

The goal to work out three to four times a week sure did sound easy enough. After all, I have maintained a regular exercise schedule since my sophomore year in college. After the requisite gaining of the freshman 15 (more like 25), my roommate Kylie and I decided to work out daily at our campus fitness facility. They offered so many classes, from yoga to spinning and rock-climbing to Tae Kwon Do, in addition to all of the usual cardio machines and free weights, that we lost the weight in no time, loved the atmosphere, and just had fun. Now, however, I haven't made it to the gym once. When I moved here several weeks ago, I joined a local fitness center that was close to my apartment, but, frankly, I've simply been too tired to think about working out at the end of the day. And now, there is no Kylie to hold me accountable. This will have to change.

And writing in my journal sure did sound like a great idea at the time! Actually, I still think it's a great idea. To journal this whole experience of becoming a teacher would be great. But, seriously, who has time? Even someone like me who has journaled on and off for years, loving words and stories, simply can't do it when there is so much other work to be done. I'm already bringing papers home to grade almost every night and am finding myself staying up a bit too late most nights finalizing tomorrow's lesson plans. So much for the planning period I've got. How do teachers do it? That's something I definitely have to ask Nathaniel about.

And Sundays! Sundays have always been a day of family, food, and fellowship for me. Growing up, Sunday meant going to church, big family dinners, and fun. We were encouraged to complete our homework and chores before Sunday so that our minds could rest and we could prepare physically and mentally for the coming week. I never saw my parents work on Sundays, and they impressed how necessary it is to living a fulfilled life. But me? Now? Well, there's only been one Sunday so far, and I bombed it completely. Exhausted from the first week of school and the rushing around of shopping and errands on Saturday coupled with binging on "Orange is the New Black" until the wee hours of the morning, I slept until almost noon. When I finally did wake up, I was struck by how there were only a few hours left in the day.

Knowing that I had failed miserably on my personal goals, I worked like a maniac for the rest of the day. I picked my clothes out for Monday and prepared and packed my healthy lunch. I wrote a paragraph (well, actually three sentences) in my journal. I even managed to take a 20-minute walk (not exactly exercise but better than nothing). I had a small sense of accomplishment and tried to give myself permission to enjoy the rest of the day, when suddenly I felt sad. My familiar expectations of Sundays as family, food, and fellowship seemed to be over. I was alone. Although I could FaceTime my friends, text my family, and even call my mom, the Sunday feeling was gone. As this sense of nostalgia crept over me, I thought I would cry. Then, I reminded myself that this was my choice. I have chosen this life.

Don't be so hard on yourself. You can still have your Sunday. You can find a new church, you can make new friends, and you can invite them to Sunday brunch. You can make better use of your Saturdays and you can salvage your Sundays, with a plan. And as soon as I thought about a plan, I began to think about Monday's lesson plans and the stack of ungraded English 9 papers that still needed grading. And that was it. I was now working on Sunday too.

It's now 11:30 P.M. Friday night. Tonight's reflections have left me both nostalgic and encouraged. I am exhausted, but also looking forward to fishing with Nathaniel tomorrow morning. It is the start of our "formal" conversations. I have a few questions for him. I'm sure he will provide some great insight.

Part II

CHAPTER 6

Essential First Lessons

Nathaniel

Laguna Madre is a long, narrow lagoon that is one of the prime fishing spots in North America. It's about five miles wide, 80 miles long and averages 3.5 feet deep. There is an upper and lower section, and we are located at the top of the lower section. You could fall out of a boat and stand up in just about any location. The water is more salty than normal sea water because it's so shallow, and has no major river flowing into it. People from around the world come here to fish.

The marina where we launch the boat has one boat ramp and eight rows of boat slips that contain boats of all sizes. Most of the boats here are flat bottom boats because of the shallow water. Mine is one of the smaller ones, but it's perfect for me. There aren't many fly fishermen here. Most of the people use rod and reels. Meghan and I could do that, but we both love to fly fish and I enjoy the challenge.

Row house condos line two sides of the marina; it reminds me of some of the neighborhoods back in Philly—the difference being that these are on the water. The units are multi-story and connected to each other. Each one has a deck on the top level and a boat slip on the bottom level. Each is painted a different color and some are more weathered than others. I often see kids fishing from the boat slips. These houses give this place a distinctive feel; I've always thought it would be fun to own one.

As I wait here in the parking lot next to Bill's Bait Shop, I can't help but get a little excited about the opportunity to use this time with Meghan to help her be a great teacher . . . and I might learn a thing or two along the way. I love this time of day. It's such a great feeling knowing I'm up and about to go fishing before most people are even awake. We will be out on the water soon. There's nothing better. Here she is. Right on time.

"Welcome to Laguna Madre," I say. "This is one of the best places in the world to fish. Like you, I had never gone fly fishing in salt water until I got here. As I said before, this place is part of the reason I moved down here right after college. Unlike standing on the side of the bank and hoping we land our fly in the area where fish might be located, we will be site fishing. In other words, we will be able to see where the fish are located. The water we will be fishing in is very shallow."

"And we will be doing that in a boat?" Meghan asks.

"Yes, we will be using *Suzy Q* over here. I bought her 22 years ago. She is a 16-foot Flats Boat."

I go on to describe the boat to Meghan and the basics of how we will be using her. "Notice her flat bottom. The motor will get us close to where the fish are feeding. The amazing thing about these boats is that you can go in water as shallow as six to eight inches. That's extreme and the conditions have to be just right, but I've done it, so I know it can be done. Once we get close to where we will fish, we will turn off the motor. The fish are very jittery when they are feeding in shallow, clear water. The way the boat is designed, one of us will fish at a time. The smaller platform up front is where you will stand to fish. I will be on this platform here in the back of the boat and use the long pole to push us along. The platform is elevated so I can locate the fish. I will then direct you to where they are feeding. There will be times we can see their tails in the air as they feed. The key will be to lay the fly out right in front of them without spooking them. You're going to love it."

"Sounds amazing," Meghan replies. "I don't want to be the only one to fish. You will fish too. Right?"

"Yes, I will fish at some point when you get the hang of it. To tell you the truth, standing on that platform and locating the fish for the person fishing is very cool. I think you will enjoy that as well. We'll get to that at some point."

"Okay, sounds good. What type of bait will we use? What type of fish will we be fishing for?" Meghan asks.

I can tell she is excited, and I reply, "The flies we will use are crab pattern, baitfish pattern, shrimp pattern. There are many types of fish, but we will typically catch catfish, black drum, red drum, sea trout, and flounder. Who knows, we might even catch a few blacktip sharks."

"This is awesome. I'm ready to get started!" Meghan exclaims.

"One more factor we will have to consider is the tide. That will dictate where we go and how deep the water will be. We will also get out of the boat and fish standing in the water. You will be amazed how big the fish can be in two feet of water. I have a rod and an old pair of Suzy's waders you can use. I also brought you a pair of polarized sunglasses that will help you see the fish in the water. Let's get going."

Looking a bit surprised, Meghan says, "Wow, you didn't have to do that. I have my sunglasses right here."

Smiling, I say, "You will love these and see pretty quickly how well they work. They will be much better than regular glasses."

"Well thanks!" Meghan says.

The sun is just rising and several other boats are launching at the same time. I start the motor and we're off. I can imagine she's taking it all in. It's hard to believe a body of water this large averages only a few feet deep. It takes about fifteen minutes to get to our first fishing spot. I think we'll anchor the boat, get our waders on and try our luck that way.

As I turn the engine off, Meghan turns around, smiles and says, "This place is unbelievable! I can't believe how big it is. And I'm going to be able to stand up to fish?"

Laughing I say, "Yep, it's kinda crazy. There are a few places it would be over your head, but we won't fish those areas much."

I can tell Meghan is still not quite sure about standing in the middle of this big body of water. So I get my waders on and slide off the boat. I land, and she laughs as the water level is just above my knees.

I say, "I don't blame you. I was pretty unsure the first time I came out here."

We get our gear ready and Meghan gets in the water. We begin to cast our lines and I can tell she is a bit rusty. I coach her a little, and she gets the hang of it after a couple of minutes. She's going to have to contend with the wind, but she will figure it out. I'm ready to hear how she's doing and what questions she has for me.

Feeling like it's a good time to begin, I say, "I'm interested to hear about how everything is going for you. Remember, we said that you would come with questions and I would hopefully be able to answer them at some level. Afterwards, it would be good if you can reflect on what we discuss and write down a few takeaways on these exit slips here. It doesn't have to be too formal. Simply write your reflections and keep them in a place where you can refer to them if you want. So, what questions do you have for me today?"

Meghan pauses from casting and looks over at me. I see the emotion in her eyes as she says, "We're two weeks into the school year and I'm struggling to keep it all together. I'm exhausted every night. I know we've talked and you have certainly seen me running around like a chicken with her head cut off trying to do it all. I feel like I'm screwing up right and left. I don't know if they respect me." She pauses to collect herself. "Does it ever get better? Do all teachers feel like this when they first start their careers? What do I need to do to manage it all?

"The first thing I want to tell you is that it WILL get better. What you are going through is very normal. We've been watching you, and you are holding it together better than you think . . . at least in front of all of us at school. I've come to the realization that teachers go through what I would call seasons during their careers. We all experience ups and downs and different phases of frustration and satisfaction along the way. You are clearly in that first season of teaching where we struggle just to 'keep our heads above water.'"

As she continues casting, Meghan says, "That's exactly how I feel. Did you feel this way when you first started?"

"Absolutely!" I reply, smiling. "That first year of teaching for me was like keeping my head above water in a very rough sea. I was insecure, filled with self-doubt, professionally naive and seemingly eternally exhausted. The first day of school was August 16th that year. I remember being so nervous and excited as school started. I was eager to meet all of the kids and to make a difference in their lives. I taught three sections of English 9, was a football coach, sponsor of the yearbook, and finally, I had lunch duty. I realized very quickly that I needed to understand who I was—not only as a teacher, but as a person.

"Like you, and all young teachers coming into teaching at age 23 straight out of college, I wanted to change the world. I thought I had all the answers. After all, I'd had the most 'cutting edge' methods classes, was young and strong and 'on fire' for being the best teacher ever. And, since I had never really failed at anything, I thought, *how hard could this teaching thing be*? Boy was I in for a rude awakening, because it was hard. And mostly it was hard because I had absolutely no idea who I was as a teacher.

"There is no way that we can understand really who we are in doing anything until we actually are in that place. For example, I can know a lot about swimming, but until I jump into the pool and try to swim, I cannot know what it's like to be a swimmer. I can know a lot about building a house, but until I actually build one, I cannot know what it's like to be a builder. The same is true of teaching. I can know, and did know, a lot about teaching . . . I knew child development theories. I knew teaching methods. I knew how to write the perfect lesson plan. I knew curriculum models. I knew content. I knew how to manage students. I knew about appropriate discipline. I knew everything that I thought I needed to know about being a teacher . . . except for one thing. I wasn't a teacher yet."

At that moment, Meghan gets her first bite and yells, "Wow, it's a big one, I think."

I reel my line in quickly and encourage her as she works to reel it in. After a good five to seven minutes, Meghan sees the sea trout on the end of the line and begins yelling, "Oh my gosh! Oh my gosh! It's huge! I've never seen a trout that big."

I secure the fish in the net and allow her to release the fly from its mouth and hold it in her hands as I take a picture with her phone. She then gently lowers it into the water. It thrashes its tail and swims away quickly. We look at each other, exchange a high five, and Meghan says, "That was awesome!"

"There are plenty more out there just like that one."

We begin casting again and I continue, "Until that first day of my first teaching position, I did not know who I was as a teacher. And knowing about disciplining kids and knowing about class management has absolutely nothing to do with actually knowing discipline and knowing class management, because now you must do it.

"I have a funny story about the difference in knowing the theory behind classroom management and actually making sound decisions managing your classroom. I really screwed up early on in this area and learned a significant lesson. In my teacher preparation program in college, we never had a class on any of this. I think it was just assumed that this would come naturally to us. Boy, were they wrong . . . at least with me. Within the first couple of months of my teaching, I seemed to be able to maintain order in my classroom. I remembered the 'don't smile until Christmas' rule and the 'if you don't come down hard on them in the beginning, you can't do it later' rule."

Smirking, Meghan replies, "I've definitely heard both of them and I had a few teachers growing up who abided by both of them. In fact, I swear one of them invented the 'don't smile' rule, but she continued past Christmas until the end of the year. She was not a happy person."

I nod in agreement. "I was so naive and insecure that first year. I asked Robert, one of the veteran teachers in my department, 'How do you handle discipline problems?' His reply was to have kids write an essay. I thought to myself, well, that sounds like a good idea. So, I was abiding by these rules fairly well. Until Philip entered my class. Philip was a new kid to our school and became quite popular with other kids rather quickly. In my class, he seemed to always be talking, outgoing and friendly. However, one day things changed dramatically.

First, I made a typical first-year teacher mistake. I turned my back on my class and I wrote on the board. Apparently, this was enough time for trouble to break out in the class. I heard quite a commotion and turned around quickly to see Philip stand up and punch another kid in the chest. Without a single thought in my head of what to do, I screamed 'Philip!' to which he yelled back at me, 'What?!!!!!' Immediately, there was absolute silence in the room as all eyes were on me now. I had never so much as raised my voice at all with my students, so this must have been shocking to them. All I could think of was to say, 'Philip. Write me an essay!'

"I didn't ask for an explanation from him or the other kid. I didn't stop to try to understand what was happening. I didn't send them to the principal's office. I simply yelled at him to 'Write me an essay!!!!' I could silently hear my fellow teacher, Robert, congratulating me in my head for handling this situation well. And then Philip yelled back, 'How many words?!!!!!' Still full of myself and wanting to show my authority, I yelled at him '5,000 words!!!!!'

Meghan looks at me and says, "Whoa."

"I know," I reply.

I continue, "Then I'm thinking, what? 5,000 words? Was I crazy? Had I lost it completely? Well, yes, I had. I had lost it completely. But I thought that I had handled it in the only way I knew how. I had to establish my authority and demonstrate command of the situation. I had done what Robert had suggested. I had assigned an essay of ridiculous length to teach them all. Let that be a lesson to them. No one would dare be disruptive in my classes again after news of this got out. Well, you could have heard the proverbial pin drop at that point. I had terrified all of my students, and silence remained for the rest of our class time. I went home thinking that today had been a whopping success. However, I could not have been more wrong.

"That night, my phone rang. It was my principal asking to see me the next morning before school. I actually was excited. I thought she was going to congratulate me on my strong discipline tactics. Boy was I wrong. When I got to school the next day, I was met in the principal's office by not only the principal, but also the vice principal of discipline along with Philip and both of his parents. My confidence wavered as I entered the office, but I held out hope that this meeting was to have Philip apologize to me with his parents' support. Again, wrong.

"As it turned out, what had occurred in my classroom with Philip punching the other student was simply what had grown out of two weeks of being bullied. For two weeks, since arriving at his new school, Philip had been teased and even threatened by students who also were in my class. Philip was a tall, athletic 9th grader who, unbeknownst to me, had quite a reputation as a basketball player and, apparently, was considered a threat to other students on our basketball team. His ability as a high school freshman meant that some of the seniors might lose their starting roles.

"What I didn't know was that just prior to my class that day, Philip had been challenged in the hallway to a fight with another student. That other student was also in my class and, in fact, had actually hit Philip in the back of his head while my back was turned to the class. As the principal explained all of this to me, my heart sank. What I had actually seen was Philip defending himself against an unprovoked assault by another student. If I wasn't so focused on controlling my class and worrying my students might take advantage of my inexperience, I might have cared enough to find out the real story before handing out such a severe punishment.

"What a lesson I learned that day! Although a long story, it ended with Philip apologizing to me, and his parents agreed that respecting the teacher was important. They agreed that he should write an essay. However, the length was reduced to 250 words. The vice principal of discipline had already called a meeting with the other student who started the fight and his parents. Then, as I sat in shame and silence having humiliated myself through my actions, my principal spoke on my behalf. She explained to Philip's parents and to Philip that I was a new teacher and that this was simply a rookie mistake. She explained that, like most first year teachers, I was learning about class management and discipline. She asked them all to have compassion for me. She assured them it wouldn't happen again and that I would be working more closely with our vice principal in charge of discipline in future situations similar to this.

"I sat there humiliated. I swallowed my pride and offered my sincere apologies to Philip and his parents, and they accepted. I accepted the advice of my principal and told the VP that I would be spending some time with him soon.

"The meeting ended and I went to my classroom, closed the door, sat at my desk, put my head down, and was totally frustrated with myself. I was shaken. I was wrong. But, I vowed that I would never again put myself in such a position. I was thankful that Philip's parents were people of integrity who showed compassion on this naive, rookie teacher. If it happened today, things might have turned out quite differently. I often wonder what happened to Philip. I'm fairly sure he doesn't remember me, but I've never forgotten that very big lesson I learned so long ago because of him."

Trying to somehow make me feel better about the situation, Meghan offers, "I could see myself doing something like that."

I chuckle and say, "I doubt it. I didn't have a clue, and I hope you learn from my mistake."

I continue, "While we are on classroom management, I was also given the advice as a young teacher that I needed to have a clear set of rules and post them where everyone could see them. I was told you need to have consequences for those rules so there is no questioning and you won't be perceived as playing favorites. Boy, did I have a great set of rules and expectations, and I laid out the consequences for breaking those rules. My attitude was this was my classroom and I was going to run a tight ship where students would abide by the rules I set forth. My advice to you is that you need to do just the opposite of what I did. I found that I was living in a black and white world where there was no room for grey.

"I've learned many things in my career, but one of the most important aspects of working with teenagers is there is a great deal of grey. Life is a series of extenuating circumstances, and if you live in a black and white world, you will certainly miss the opportunity to truly make a difference in the lives of the students you teach. Every student is different and there are many reasons for their behaviors and attitudes. For example, I have learned that there are times when you have to give some students a little extra time on assignments."

"I spent a good bit of time developing my classroom rules,"

Meghan says. "I also feel you need some rules that are 'set in stone' and not negotiable. So, what do you think about that?"

"Honestly," I reply, "I learned this the hard way. A sophomore in my second year of teaching named Anthony Davis didn't have a father in his life, and his mother was a drug addict. He came to me on more than one occasion and indicated that he didn't have time to complete all of his assignments because his mother was nowhere to be found and he had to take care of his two younger siblings. That included making sure they were fed, bathed, put to bed in a timely manner and finally back to school the next morning. My response to this situation was that I didn't want this kid to take advantage of me, and I needed to stick to my rule that homework was due on the date I indicated, and the consequence would be a subsequent zero if you didn't meet that expectation. I felt bad for him and told him that I was sorry. But if I made an exception for him, I would have to do it for any student who had an excuse for not turning in their work.

"Anthony failed my class that year and ultimately quit school in the middle of his junior year. I saw him later that summer. He was leaving a convenience store while I was filling my car with gas. I said hello and asked how he was doing. He said he was doing okay, but he was working at a job he really didn't like. His brother and sister were in foster care and he was living in an apartment with his mother. We talked for a few minutes, and after he left, it hit me that I could have been a contributing factor in his decision to drop out of school.

"It was a sinking feeling, and I began to question my rationale and methods of accountability. What if I had been more understanding? What if I had worked with him and allowed him to have a different timeline than the other students based on his circumstance? What if I had been more patient with him? What if I had taken the time to get to know him better and understand what he was experiencing? He might have passed my class. I might have been able to help him stay in school. I wanted to chase him down and apologize. I wanted to say I was sorry for letting him down. It is one of those situations that truly made an impact on me.

"I would encourage you to have as few rules as possible and avoid stating your consequences ahead of time. Some teachers I know have only one rule: 'Don't do anything that is detrimental to you, the people in our classroom, or this school.' If you break that rule, there will be a consequence. And by not stating the consequence ahead of time, the teacher has the ability to provide a consequence that is appropriate for that particular situation. That covers every possible situation that might arise. The expectation is clear, and the teacher has the flexibility to be a leader.

"I don't know if you noticed, but I don't have any rules posted in my classroom. I only have three values posted: Respect, Attitude, and Effort. My belief is that you don't need lots of rules, and stating consequences ahead of time will only cause you to back yourself into a corner where you have no opportunity to take into consideration those extenuating circumstances.

"I believe that if you treat others with respect and you display a positive attitude and you work to your potential, good things will happen to you and we will have a great learning environment in the classroom. We talk about what those values mean and what they look like in action on the first day of class. I have learned to recognize when I observe the values being lived out in the classroom. That might be a simple 'well done,' silent thumbs up, or a recognition in front of the class, depending on the student and the situation. Just remember, you are not really a leader in the classroom if you are a slave to a long list of rules and stated consequences."

Meghan stops fishing, turns around and says, "Your story about Anthony is sad. I could see myself doing the same thing. I've always thought that you have to be consistent, and if you don't treat everyone the same when it comes to discipline, you will lose credibility with the students."

Smiling, I respond, "You have to be consistent in your expectations of classroom behavior. In other words, you should expect that all students will embrace the values and/or follow the rules you have established. The difference lies in how you handle each student based on the circumstances. I'm sure you've heard it before, but students should be treated equitably rather than equally. You will hold everyone accountable, but handle the discipline according to the situation."

"Makes sense," Meghan replies.

"Another aspect of teaching that I struggled with in that first year of teaching was the type of relationship I should have with my students. I got advice about this almost immediately from the other teachers in the Language Arts Department. There were four of us including our department chair, Jim Tingle. We were talking about this during one of our department meetings very early in the year and Jim was the most vocal about the topic. How can I describe Jim? He was a 25-year veteran teacher and had been a department chair for five years before I arrived. He was not a pleasant man. He didn't seem to like anyone. He didn't like the students. He didn't like his co-workers. He didn't like the staff. I'm not sure he liked himself. He just seemed to be a miserable man. I remember thinking, *how can this man be a department chair and teach high school kids every day when he doesn't enjoy any part of it*?

"I do believe there was a time when Jim was a highly effective teacher who had a passion for kids and the profession, but he regularly demonstrated far less patience and flexibility in his work while I worked with him. Bless her soul, my mother would politely yet pointedly refer to Jim and those like him as 'an opinion looking for an issue.' For example, when someone asked Jim why he never became an administrator, he perked up and loudly stated, 'Because I was never willing to have the operation that requires removal of half of your brain and your entire spine!' "

Meghan snickers and says, "That's a good one. I haven't heard that line before."

"It is kinda funny if you think about it," I reply. "I know Jim wasn't necessarily talking about our administrators or even administrators in general, but it did tend to foster an 'us and them' mentality which was certainly not helpful. It hasn't helped during my tenure at Delmar. To me, it was his way to deal with a road not taken previously in his career. The idea of being a principal or assistant principal has never held any appeal for me. My classroom is my haven, but please know I have tremendous respect for those who choose to take on the role, and especially for those who do it well.

"I'm getting off topic a bit, but something else that bothered me about Jim was how he would mock other teachers who took their roles very seriously. He would make snide remarks and make fun when they weren't around. He never did it in their presence. I often thought, *What must this guy say when I'm not around*? One teacher in our department who was a regular target of his cynical remarks was Dana Lupido. Dana is the most professional teacher I have ever worked with during my career. She was the complete opposite of Jim. She loved teaching. She loved the students she taught and was always available for a colleague who had a question. She couldn't have been nicer to me and more helpful. She was there any time I needed help or advice. I have so much more to tell you about Dana."

Meghan has stopped fishing and is sitting on the boat. She opens the thermos and pours a cup of coffee and offers it to me.

"Thanks," I say.

She pours herself a cup and says, "Dana sounds like a great teacher. I definitely would like to hear more about her. Jim, on the other hand, sounds like a bit of a whack job and shouldn't be teaching kids."

I nod in agreement. "Jim's attitude was that he could care less if his students liked him. He felt students would take advantage of you as an authority figure if it was important that they liked you. Dana viewed this relationship differently than Jim. She agreed the most important factor for credibility as a teacher was that your students respect you. She said you can and probably should demand respect for the position of teacher—meaning, the teacher can demand that students listen if you are talking or respect their peers in the classroom. However, she felt you had to work every day to earn their respect as a teacher they wanted to follow. She firmly believed in the adage that students fall into one of three categories when it comes to motivation and buy-in. They view tasks or requirements as 'have to,' 'get to,' or 'want to.' If you choose to view tasks as 'I have to,' your level of commitment and engagement will not be very high. The reality is that we all have tasks and requirements of us every day.

"However, you can choose to look at them differently. Dana would argue that if someone looked at a task as 'I get to,' that person would have a much higher level of engagement and commitment. The person looks at it as more of a privilege, and he or she will receive some type of reward for accomplishing the task. Finally, 'I want to' do a task is the ultimate in self-motivation. The motivation is clearly internal and the person views it as something that is enjoyable and rewarding simply for the sake of doing it. Her thought was that if students bought into you because you earned their respect and they moved from 'have to' towards 'get to' or even 'want to,' you were going to be a great teacher because those students were more self-motivated.

"She also felt that it didn't have to be an either/or situation. In other words, many teachers feel students either respect you or they like you. She truly believed that if they respect and like you, they will follow you. According to Dana, the best teachers have both, and if they have to sacrifice one, they will sacrifice being liked every time. It can't be your goal that everyone likes you all the time. You won't hold them accountable. Her message to me was that there will be times when your students don't like you because you are making them do something they don't generally enjoy doing or you are holding them accountable for poor behavior. But in the end, they need to like something about the person in the front of the room who is trying to help them learn. She firmly believed that students don't learn from teachers they don't like.

"My advice for you in this area is to understand that your students will not like you every day if you are doing your job. And you might not like them every day. But you can earn their respect and be likable at the same time. In fact, if you think about it, most of the students we teach don't have the emotional maturity to distinguish between respect and like. Just ask one of them to tell you about Mr. or Mrs. ________ and they will almost always say, 'I like her' or 'I don't like him.' When asked to explain further, you realize they describe qualities they either respect or don't respect. I would argue that the very best teachers develop meaningful relationships with their students, and you will often hear their students say they respected their teachers and didn't necessarily like them every day, but they loved being taught by them."

"Honestly," Meghan says, "I think my problem is less about demanding they all respect me and more that I want them all to like me. I know that isn't ideal and I have already experienced a couple of the students taking advantage of that. I know I want to develop meaningful relationships with them. I guess I just need to figure out a balance."

Trying to encourage her, I reply, "You will figure out the balance that works for you. It might take time, but you will get to that point."

"I sure hope so," Meghan responds.

"One last aspect of this season I would like to discuss is something that took me a while to realize. Let me ask you a question. How many students in our various classes will grow up and become Language Arts teachers like us?"

"I don't know. I haven't even thought about it," Meghan responds. "Why do you ask?"

"I would say that less than two percent of the kids in our classes will become teachers, and even less than that will become Language Arts teachers. I say this because the overwhelming majority of our students don't automatically love our subject matter. We wake up thinking about it, eat our lunch thinking about it, go to bed thinking about it, and they only think about it when they are with us and when they are doing the work we require of them. Even then, many are distracted and not fully engaged. It used to frustrate me that they didn't care as much as I did. I would encourage you to keep this in mind as you go throughout your day. It's easy to teach that one to two percent who will be like us. The challenge is to create an environment where the other 98 percent look forward to coming to our classrooms and learning what we teach. The sooner you embrace this idea, the less frustrated you will be and the more you and your students will enjoy the experience you have together.

"The first season of teaching is interesting and challenging. You will make many mistakes and potentially have regrets. However, you will get through it. Hopefully, you have a few takeaways from this first fishing trip. At some point in the next few days, write on the exit slip what you would say are the three most important points you took from our conversation today."

We pack up all of our gear and head back to the marina. I'm feeling good about our first outing and I think Meghan has a few takeaways she can think about. I don't want to come across as if I have all of the answers. I just want her to think and question.

As she is getting into her car to head home for what I am sure will be a good nap, Meghan turns and says, "Thanks again for a great morning. I'm whipped but had a great time. See you on Monday."

Meghan

Boy, do I feel better. And spending time learning from the best while fishing has got to be some kind of first for a new teacher. I was afraid it was going to be awkward. Alone with a person I barely know fishing and talking. But surprisingly, it wasn't. I guess our shared love of fishing has created a kind of bond between us already. I think this experience will be great.

He wants to know what I learned? Well, a lot more than what I will put down on today's exit slip. I learned that he's human. I guess since he is the Texas Teacher of the Year, I had this image of a teacher who had never struggled. But instead, not only has he struggled, he is so honest in sharing those struggles with me.

He sure did make me think about the management stuff. I thought the more rules the better, and yet, it seems clear that less is more. And I'm going to be more intentional in planning for a response to discipline issues before they happen. I don't want to be caught off guard like he was with that student, Philip.

There is so much I can learn from this man. His willingness to share his stories of when he felt swamped and overwhelmed was not only helpful, but he also made them funny. It makes me realize that one day I will look back on this period in my life and laugh at my old stories too. Can't wait for next time!

EXIT SLIP NUMBER ONE

1. *I have discovered that I am not alone in this journey, and it is normal to feel frustrated, scared, and overwhelmed at this point in my career.*
2. *This too shall pass. I believe you when you say it will get better for me and the students I teach.*
3. *My focus is very much on me instead of the students right now as I try to "keep my head above water." I hope I am able to make the shift to focusing more on the students.*

Nathaniel

As I pull into my driveway and park the boat in the barn, I'm excited to share with Suzy about the first fishing trip. I walk through the back door and she's loading the dishwasher. She turns with a big smile and asks, "Hey, how'd it go? Did you actually take her to a few of your favorite spots, or like most people, did she get the spots where you have to be really lucky to get any bites?"

I laugh as I give her a kiss. "Yes, I took her to two of my favorites. I think she had a great time. She's a good kid and a natural fisherman. You can tell she's been fishing many times. She said it had been a few years, but it was just like riding a bike for her."

"That's great," Suzy replies. "I'm proud of you for actually allowing her to experience your favorite spots. How did the teaching lessons go?"

"I actually think it went well," I reply. "We talked about the mistakes I made in that first year. I wish I would have had someone talk to me about this stuff in my first year of teaching. I think it might have prevented me from doing such emotional and mental harm to some of those students. Talking with Meghan reminded me that I was not a very good teacher that first year. I also love her excitement and enthusiasm for learning. She is overwhelmed right now, but she wants to be a great teacher. I'm going to enjoy spending these Saturdays with her. You are more than welcome to come with us, you know. You would have so much to offer her as well."

Suzy smiles and says, "Thanks, but I'll let that be your time with her. Maybe we can have her over for lunch or dinner. She would probably enjoy a home-cooked meal and not have to eat alone."

"That's a great idea," I reply. "I'll mention that and see what she thinks."

"Good. How about that nice big 'Honey-do' list on the table over there? Maybe you can knock a few of those off today," Suzy says with a wink.

I wrap Suzy with a hug, kiss her forehead, and say, "At least two!"

CHAPTER 7

Brick Walls and Bumps in the Road

Meghan

I'm excited to finally meet Suzy later today. It was nice of Nathaniel to invite me to lunch after we finish this morning. It's still dark as I arrive and as I turn the headlights off, I notice Nathaniel has already backed the boat down the ramp. I grab my sunglasses and hat and head over to the dock. "What a beautiful morning," I say as I walk up to the ramp and start to release the boat from the trailer.

As Nathaniel starts the engine, he responds, "We are so lucky to be able to fish at a place like this. Suzy and I are looking forward to having you over for lunch later today. She was excited on Thursday when I told her I had invited you for today. She will have something great prepared for us. Hope you will be hungry."

With a huge grin on my face and rubbing my stomach, I say, "Can't wait. I ate just a granola bar this morning, so I could save room for lunch."

Cutting the engine, Nathaniel says, "Great. It will be fun." He continues, "You did pretty well last time. I have a feeling you will do even better today." He then asks, "You want to handle the motor this time? I can direct you where we need to go."

"Would love to," I reply with a smile. "I was wondering last time if I would get a chance to do that."

"Great," Nathaniel responds. "How about if we start with teaching you how to back the boat off the trailer? It isn't busy this morning, so now would be a great time."

I get in the boat and manage to back it out with his help, and then pull up next to the dock. He ties the boat to the dock and then parks the truck and trailer in the parking lot. I look around and notice how still everything is at this time of the morning. The sun is just starting to peek above the horizon and I think, *How beautiful is this place*?

As Nathaniel unties the boat and steps on board, he says, "You're a few months into this teaching thing. What questions do you have for me today?"

"I'm truly glad it's Saturday," I reply. "This week was a tough one. Maybe it's the upcoming Fall Break. I have to admit I seem to be ready for a break as much as my students. You know, just when I seem to feel like I'm settling in and feeling pretty good about my teaching, I encounter a roadblock. Is this what happens to everyone this time of year? I hope not. When I feel like this, I seem to be almost counting the days until a longer winter break."

Nathaniel gives me a brief tutorial on how to operate the motor and we are off. It's hard to describe the feeling as the wind hits me in the face. I see the loons in the marsh to my right and they take flight as we pass by them. The anticipation of catching lots of fish is exciting. Nathaniel sits up front and just points the direction he wants me to go as we navigate through the various channels before heading to more open water. Once we get out into open water, he holds his hand up and I slow down.

We get our fishing gear ready and Nathaniel says, "There is definitely a predictable rhythm to the school year. You stick with this long enough and you'll learn those weeks and months where you will feel settled in and kids will seem to be learning, and then there are those other times either leading up to or right after holidays or breaks in the schedule when none of us can find our bearings. Over time you will know how to navigate through those periods more smoothly. For now, though, I want to focus on something that you just mentioned. You said 'when I encounter a roadblock.' What do you consider a roadblock? How would you define that?"

"Well, to me a roadblock would be something that stands in my way of achieving a goal," I reply. "It's the 'you can't get there from here' moment when you realize that your path to success is blocked. It's an immovable object and there is nothing that I can do about it. For example, yesterday I got the memo about the fire drill. But, really? Did it have to happen ten minutes into 3rd period? That's my most challenging English 9 class. That class always enters loudly and I seem to have to work extra hard to get them settled down, and just when we seemed to be in a good rhythm yesterday, there was the fire drill.

"Of course I'd forgotten about it, which only added to my frustration. The students were thrilled. And, out we went. Once outside, my class acted like they were 3rd graders at recess. I honestly was frustrated and embarrassed as all the other classes seemed to be behaving. When they finally rang the bell to re-enter the building, we got back to the classroom and three students were missing. How does that happen? They did show up about five minutes later. But, the point is, my whole lesson was shot. I couldn't get them to settle down with only about 12 minutes left in the period. So, I basically gave up. I just sat down and they carried on. And, honestly I didn't even care. I feel really horrible about it now. So, the fire drill was a roadblock to me getting where I wanted to go. I wanted to teach my lesson."

Nathaniel chuckles. "Ah, fire drills! One of my absolute favorite interruptions. I remember my first one like it was yesterday; feeling like the kids would be out of control outside without four walls to keep them contained. I want to challenge you about your thinking of roadblocks. I can't explain it any better than Randy Pausch did in the *Last Lecture*. You probably don't know much about Randy, but he was a professor at Carnegie-Mellon. He was diagnosed with terminal pancreatic cancer and was asked to give the Last Lecture, a prized lecture given by a distinguished professor at his university. You can find the entire lecture on YouTube.

"Although he died at a young age, he left an amazing legacy. Randy explained what he called the 'brick walls.' That would be similar to your roadblocks. The way Randy saw it, the brick walls in our lives aren't there to keep the other people out. The brick walls are there to help us realize how much we really want something. In your case, the fire drill was the brick wall. On the other side of the wall were your lesson and your students' learning. But you allowed the brick wall to keep you out. You allowed the fire drill to stop you from teaching. So really the brick wall—that fire drill—is a test. It's a test to see how badly you want to teach and how badly you want your students to learn."

At this point, we aren't having any luck in this spot and Nathaniel says, "We should try our luck somewhere else."

So, we head to another spot around the bend and stop in a place that looks like something out of a movie or a Hemingway novel. The sea grass is swaying in the wind, the herons are walking on the water's edge, and the air smells distinctly salty.

Nathaniel continues, "Let me tell you what I've learned from some of my brick walls over the years. Years ago I made up my mind that no brick walls would stop me from teaching or from my students learning. I learned that I had to figure out how to get over the brick walls. For example, the fire drill situation. Schools will always have fire drills. There is no getting around it. But rather than focusing on what you can't get done and what can't happen when the fire drill alarm sounds, focus on what you can do and what can happen. Here's what I do. First of all, I pay very close attention to the timing of the fire drills. And then I strategically plan exactly what I'll have the students do before, during, and after the drill. You know, there is nothing that says that all the learning has to happen in the classroom.

"What about learning during the fire drill? What about giving them a task before the drill and then having them work on it with a partner? You could do a think, pair and share while they are standing outside. My role outside is to hold my students accountable just as it is inside the classroom. Then once we come back in, those last few minutes can be to share and refine what was being intentionally taught and intentionally learned despite the fire drill."

"Really?" I ask. "Does that work? When did you come up with this idea? Did someone tell you this like you are telling me?"

"No," Nathaniel responds. "No one told me. I began to settle into teaching after the first couple of years, and I became more stabilized in how I approached the craft of teaching. I began to realize that time was short with much to learn. I also began to realize that my students deserved better from me than me being a babysitter on days when there were fire drills or assemblies. Yes, assemblies. They can be one of those brick walls.

"After I got through those first years of feeling overwhelmed and continually floundering to a point where I felt I was finding my way, I began to realize that if I was going to make it, I needed to hone the craft of teaching. By realizing this was possible, I began to feel a bit of success as a teacher. I think this happens to many teachers once the instability of those first couple of years passes. If they are still standing and haven't quit, they will ease into a time of stability in their teaching. You know somewhere around 50% of teachers quit within their first three to five years of teaching. That number is unacceptable as far as I'm concerned."

I shake my head as I continue to search for that first fish of the day. "That's a really high percentage. I'm looking forward to getting to that point where I don't feel so overwhelmed. Tell me more about what that's like."

"Some of the feelings I just mentioned begin to happen," Nathaniel replies. "There is a subtle realization that the art of teaching is coming easier to you. Your lesson plans are established and only need minor tweaking rather than complete rewrites. Your class management routines have been fine-tuned. It's no longer trial and error with what will work or not work. Often, this coincides with an awareness that you really are beginning to connect with more of your students.

"I'm not just talking about those who like you, are eager to learn and are responding. There is an increasing sense that you are doing something right in your teaching that is leading to success for more of your students. And then success breeds more success. Your self-worth as a teacher and your identity as a teacher begin to improve. Meghan, I think that most teachers are fairly unaware that this is actually happening. But I want you to be very aware of this over the next year or two. I think the more aware you are of it, the more of an impact you will make as a teacher."

"You know," I reply, "honestly, some days right now I see glimpses of this possibility for myself. Then, on other days like during this week, I think it's just not possible. Roadblocks or brick walls. Whatever we call them, I just want them to be gone."

"OK then, I guess it's time for me to explain the 'Bumps in the

Road Theory,'" Nathaniel says. "Actually, this is a little theory I made up when my children were young to help explain how to think during tough times. I want you to imagine you are driving a car. Have you ever hit a bump in the road?"

"Of course I have," I reply.

Nathaniel responds, "So, a couple of questions for you. How did you know it was there? How did you know you were approaching a bump in the road?"

"Well, sometimes I didn't see it coming. I sometimes forget about those speed bumps in the school parking lot until it's too late."

"Me too. But what if you're flying down the highway and don't see a bump and hit it going 70 miles per hour? What's going to happen to you?"

"I don't know exactly, but I don't think it would end very well."

"Exactly. So how do we know when there might be a bump in the road in front of us?"

"I guess there would be a sign. Like SLOW DOWN or BUMP or CAUTION."

"Yes! There are usually signs that we are approaching a bump in our road long before we actually come upon it. What options do you have at this point?"

"Well, the obvious one is to pay attention to the signs, to slow down, to use caution while driving."

"Absolutely. But you also have another option. And, unknowingly, many folks exercise this option. Instead of paying attention, slowing down, and learning to navigate over the bumps in their road, they choose to either ignore the signs and crash and burn. Or they choose to take a detour around the bump. Oh, they see the signs, but they tell themselves that they don't want to deal with the bump. They want to avoid it even if it means going out of their way to get around it. It's like the traffic report that tells us of the accident and the five-mile backup as we are trying to get somewhere. There are those that decide they'd rather drive 25 miles out of their way than to sit in traffic, slow down, and get beyond the backup. Here's the problem with detouring around a bump in your road. If we avoid bumps in our road by going around them, we never learn how to navigate over them.

It's almost like being in denial or burying your head in the sand. You might be avoiding the immediate bump in the road. But by doing so, you aren't learning anything about how to navigate over the bumps. So, the lesson of my Bump in the Road Theory is there will always be bumps in our road. It's just life.

"Sometimes there are signs and signals all around us that something challenging is coming our way and we do not see or we choose to ignore those signs. This often results in a crash and burn crisis on the other side. Or, we see the signs and choose to ignore the bump and navigate around the problem rather than facing it head on. We may get around that bump, but we have learned nothing about how to navigate over the next bump. So, I encourage you to look at those bumps in the road that might occur in your teaching—or in your life—as opportunities and challenges for growth. You may not like it. But if you pay attention to the signs along the way, you'll see the bump coming. If you slow down and use caution, you will learn how to gradually navigate over any type of bump you encounter. You will emerge on the other side stronger and wiser and ready to take on the next bump in your road.

"There will ALWAYS be bumps in your road. There will ALWAYS be challenges. But I believe they are placed there for a reason. I believe they are placed there for us to grow into the teachers and into the people that we've been purposed to be. There are lessons that you will learn and ways that you will grow from every bump in your road. I think the ability to begin to understand this stands between novice, struggling teachers and those who go on to make a significant difference in the lives of their students, their fellow teachers, and the profession. The beginning of this understanding seems to follow those first difficult years of survival. So, yesterday's fire drill was a bump in your teaching road. Next week, it will be something else . . . and the week after that and the week after that and the week after that. Pay attention to all that you are learning. I encourage you to pay attention to the signs. Be aware of how you navigate over each bump and take that learning forward as you progress through your teaching career.

"For some teachers, they get to this place and don't move forward. Instead, they start coasting. But those great teachers, those most impactful teachers, those teachers who you want to emulate, move through this driven to become a teacher who changes lives. I know that you can be one of those teachers, Meghan. It's in you. I always say that when we are meant to know something, it becomes made known to you. What is becoming made known to you includes the signs and the bumps in your road. So whether you consider it a roadblock, a brick wall, or a bump in the road, just remember, there is something to be learned with each one."

I think Nathaniel senses I'm getting tired of casting with no luck. I wish I had more patience at times. He says, "I think we'll call it a morning. There are those rare days when they aren't biting regardless of what you throw at 'em. I think it's time to go eat lunch."

I nod in agreement and we head back to the marina. Nathaniel has me pull the boat up to the dock so he can get the truck and back the trailer down the ramp. I don't think I could do that at this point. Glad he's behind the wheel. I maneuver the boat on to the trailer and he secures it. He pulls the boat with me in it up next to my car. I hop out and hand him the keys to the boat.

Nathaniel takes the keys and says, "Let's head to the house. Suzy is really looking forward to meeting you and, more importantly, I need you to meet her. She is going to be your special guest instructor today."

Jokingly, I respond, "Guest Instructor, I thought that was supposed to be your gig. Is this a 'Mars and Venus' thing where I need wise female counsel?"

Laughing, Nathaniel replies, "Not at all. As a younger man I always thought I was pretty smart. Then I met and married Suzy. Still haven't figured out how I pulled that one off. Over the years she has repeatedly reminded me that there are different types of intelligences. I was proud of my IQ and all the content knowledge that came with it, but she quickly taught me how lacking I was when it came to emotional intelligence. It's time for the two of you to meet."

"I can't wait." I reply. "I need to meet her just to confirm that she does indeed exist and, if so, I can't wait to see the halo above her head because she must be a saint."

Nathaniel laughs even harder and says, "Are you implying I might be hard to live with?"

I give a mischievous look and reply, "I'm just saying . . . "

"Oh, I see someone's got jokes. We woofin' on each other a little bit now?" Nathaniel asks with a grin.

"Woofin'? Where did that come from, *Happy Days* or *Welcome Back Kotter*?" I ask. "I've seen those shows on TV Land and Netflix. It is roasting or 'throwin' some shade' now, Mr. Speer, to be generationally accurate."

Showing an appreciation for my attempt at humor, Nathaniel responds, "Impressive. Fonzie and the Sweathogs would be proud of you. Let's hit the road. Follow me. We'll be there in about 20 minutes."

I think he appreciated my humor. I sure hope so, anyway. Today was beautiful. I feel happy and relaxed and reflective. The fishing wasn't as good as the first trip, but the water was calm and the scenery was incredible. The sun seemed to dance on the sheer expanse of water stretching into the biggest Laguna I've ever seen. It leaves me feeling so content today.

Who gets to do this? I mean really? I feel like I should just pinch myself sometimes. To be a first year teacher in the company of an amazing mentor out here on the water enjoying this spectacular day and, all the while, learning so much about this thing called teaching.

Brick walls and bumps in the road . . . lessons to be learned. Until today, I never really thought much about how teachers go through a process of development over time. Maybe the missing link for me was in understanding not only that this happened but, more importantly, *how* this happens. It happens through the stories of their teaching. Stories about challenges and stories about opportunities.

As I look back over this past month, I remember some tough moments. There were days when I let those moments really get to me. I allowed those difficult moments with students to defeat me. I allowed those interruptions to my plans to frustrate me to the point of just giving up. I allowed petty annoyances to kick my butt a little.

But now, I see that there is a probable purpose in every adversity. Rather than looking at those from a victim perspective, I need to change the lens through which I view them. Instead, I will really try to see them for what they are . . . opportunities for me to grow and learn and become better.

It's comforting to know that I will get there. Nathaniel believes in me. I think he believes in me more than I actually believe in myself right now. His belief in me is helpful.

I am looking forward to meeting Suzy and learning more about her experiences as a teacher. I'm sure she has a little different perspective than Nathaniel. Hope she made something for lunch that I like. I am starving.

EXIT SLIP NUMBER TWO

1. *This is the season where teachers start to get into a rhythm and figure out how to teach.*
2. *Quite a few teachers leave the profession by the time they get to this season because they understand they don't have what it takes to become a great teacher, or they realize teaching isn't for them. Maybe it's partly due to their inability to deal with the roadblocks and bumps in the road.*
3. *Teachers can remain here and perhaps become complacent or they can choose the more challenging route to becoming a great teacher.*

Nathaniel

I'm excited to have Meghan and Suzy meet. Suzy has wanted to meet her since I started discussing the idea of mentoring a young teacher. Suzy thought it was a great idea and she has encouraged me every step of the way. However, I thought it was interesting when she told me not to be surprised if the mentoring process turned out to be more challenging for me than my mentee. I immediately asked her why she thought that and what prompted her statement. She went on to tell me that I was, at this point in my career, a master teacher. She said I was an educator at the top of my profession and had likely been at that level for a number of years. I remember smiling and saying something snarky back at her about concurring with her assessment.

She then told me the problem. She challenged me that one can be an expert at something while also being a novice in regards to how to teach that skill set to someone else. She said I had worked many years to perfect my craft but during that time I probably rarely, if ever, thought about how I would teach what I know to someone else. I have informally mentored young teachers in the past, but never invested that much. She also challenged me by reminding me that I have notoriously avoided student teacher requests in the past because that scenario would just slow me down and hurt my classroom in regard to achievement gains.

To further make her point, she used the analogy of a celebrated chef who for years has cooked by feel and taste without writing any recipes down. Chef Speer then decides to take on an apprentice, which is a wonderful idea until said chef realizes that all of those wonderful recipes and all of that culinary knowledge are stored in his head! She went on to remind me of the self-reflection, recovery, and organization process I needed to do in order to effectively mentor a new teacher.

Once again she ever-so-lovingly and courteously tweaked me in the nose with reality as only Suzy can. Deep down I knew this to be true, but I never really took the time to admit to myself or have a conversation with her or anyone else about it because I felt it would make me appear inept or the opposite of accomplished . . . whatever that is. My ego kept reminding me that I was just named Texas State Teacher of the Year. It took my wife to remind me that the award didn't come with a how-to manual. That would be up to me.

That conversation is a perfect example of why Meghan needs to meet Suzy today. Suzy chuckled when I told her my protégé was female. She reminded me of the book she had us read together a few years back, *Men are Like Waffles—Women are Like Spaghetti* by Bill and Pam Farrell. The contrasting visual of waffles and spaghetti speaks for itself. Suzy wanted me to understand that we were wired differently by gender. She helped me realize I was a compartmentalizer with a lack of connection . . . like the waffle. I could avoid vulnerability by suppressing things that made me feel weak or insecure. Suzy needed connection and she needed us to be connected like spaghetti for us to truly understand each other. The gift that Suzy gave me in that process and the gift she has so often provided me over the course of our marriage is awareness and perspective. She basically called me on it.

Over the years I have come to the conclusion that a large part of Suzy's emotional intelligence, work ethic, wisdom, and ethic of care are grounded in the fact that she is trained professionally as an elementary or K–6 teacher. Grasping that reality took me years to understand because, unless you have worked as an educator in an elementary or middle school setting, one has no idea what those teachers choose to take on every day. Her school and classroom was less than half a mile away from the high school, but it might as well have been halfway across the globe, based on my knowledge and understanding of what my colleagues did every day in the pipeline grades prior to students arriving at the high school.

What I realized was that the spaghetti and waffles analogy also works regarding teachers in school systems. Elementary level is like spaghetti and secondary is like waffles. Elementary teachers seek out connection and collaboration. Secondary teachers traditionally operate in silos, avoiding connection and collaboration. The system fostered that behavior until Rick DuFour's professional learning communities work challenged those structures. His work was groundbreaking in that it encouraged secondary schools to function more like elementary schools. He emphasized connection and collaboration that supported both improved student performance and increased teacher satisfaction. Meghan needs to learn this early in her career in order to be a thoughtful and empathic colleague and educator. There is no one better to explain it to her than Suzy. Okay, here we are.

Meghan

Nathaniel says, "Hey, Meghan. Just park your car on the street. It'll be fine. Welcome to Casa de Speer! Let's go around back. We are dining on the patio."

I park the car and head towards the side of the house where I wait on Nathaniel as he puts the boat in what looks like a barn. You can tell it's very old, but it looks like it has been well maintained. As he comes out of the barn, Nathaniel smiles and says, "That barn is one of the biggest reasons I wanted to buy this place. You would be amazed at how much stuff I have in there. Barely enough room to park the boat."

We go around the side of the house to reach the patio. It looks amazing. There's a woman, who I assume is Suzy, putting the final touches on the place settings. I can smell the food as we approach and I can tell it's Mexican. I'm excited.

Nathaniel walks up to her and they give each other a smile and a quick kiss. Nathaniel puts his arm around her waist. "Suzy, I would like you to meet Ms. Meghan Donahue. Meghan, meet the love of my life and the woman who keeps me on the straight and narrow."

Suzy rolls her eyes as she reaches out her hand to shake mine and responds, "Enough, Nathaniel. Please don't go all Jerry Maguire on the poor girl. She just got here. It's a pleasure, Meghan. Welcome to our home. I've heard so much about you and have looked forward to meeting you."

Smiling, I say, "Thank you. It's a pleasure to finally meet you as well. I really appreciate the lunch invitation and I was just told this morning that you are my guest instructor today."

Suzy replies, "Oh my, please don't you worry. That is my husband's polite way of saying that someone else may be more qualified to share certain information and insights as opposed to him. Come on and sit down. I hope you like shrimp tacos."

Nathaniel interrupts, "*Tacos el camarones* for lunch . . . my favorite!"

Suzy looks at me and smirks as if to say, "Here he goes again, butchering the Spanish language."

Continuing, Suzy says, "I think it is humorously ironic that I have lived with a dedicated fisherman all of these years but if we want to eat fish I need to buy them at the market. The man lives to catch fish but would die if he could not put them back."

Nathaniel gives her a wink. We all sit down and Suzy begins, "So, how was the fishing this morning? More importantly, tell more about you and how you got here to this small town in South Texas."

Nathaniel reaches for a drink of iced tea and responds, "We didn't even smell a fish today. We had great conversation, but no fish."

Suzy says, "That happens. I'm glad you had a meaningful conversation. You will both remember that much longer than how many fish you might have caught."

Nathaniel cocks his head to the side and says, "Hmm, maybe," as if to say that might be debatable. Spoken as a true fisherman.

Suzy then says, "Dig in, let's eat." After a bite she looks at me and says, "Tell me about you, Meghan."

I proceed to tell the story of my life and how I got to this place and time. Suzy is completely engaged and asks several questions as I tell her my story between bites of delicious tacos, rice, beans, and salad. Nathaniel is sitting quietly, observing, eating, and seeming to enjoy our conversation.

After a while, Suzy begins explaining the rewards and challenges of being an elementary and middle school teacher. It's my turn to listen intently and I can tell right away she is passionate about kids and teaching.

After several minutes, Nathaniel interrupts us. "Suzy, I think you should tell her about *Men are Like Waffles—Women are Like Spaghetti*. It not only does a great job of describing the differences between men and women, it also really captures how elementary and secondary teachers differ. I know it helped me understand those differences and I think it will help Meghan as well."

I respond with a puzzled look, "Waffles and Spaghetti? What is that? Tell me about it, Suzy."

Suzy smiles. "It is actually a good analogy. It's the title of a book. I heard about it and asked Nathaniel to read it with me because I thought it would help us understand each other better in our marriage. The book uses gender differences to posit that men are like a waffle in that many times they can compartmentalize their lives into little squares resembling a waffle. The authors then suggest that the lives of most women function like spaghetti in that everything is connected somehow to everything else. They go on to say that the two perspectives have sharp contrasts, but if people can be empathic and stay mindful of their tendencies as well as the tendencies of others around them, there is a far greater likelihood to promote harmony and avoid conflict.

"It seems to me this contrast also plays out in traditional school settings. Secondary teachers, usually grades 7–12, are subject-based and certified. If you ask a high school teacher what they do, they will normally respond by saying something like, 'I teach English,' or Math, or Science. Ask the same question of an elementary teacher and you will likely hear, 'I teach 5th grade,' or 'I teach kindergarten."

Nathaniel interrupts Suzy again at this point as he looks at me. "I think her point here is that elementary tends to be like spaghetti and secondary tends to be like waffles. I didn't realize it at first, but the best answer I heard to that previous question about what someone teaches came from Suzy. When I first met her I knew she was an elementary teacher. I was nervous trying to make small talk at dinner. So I reached in my bag of skilled articulation and popped the question. 'So Suzy, what do you teach?'

She looked at me, smiled and said, "That's a silly question. I teach kids . . . the same thing that you do!"

Continuing, Nathaniel says, "I wasn't mature enough to grasp the wisdom in her answer at that specific moment, but over the years I have learned to appreciate just how wise her answer was at the time. Sometimes, Meghan, the best lessons we receive are the ones we don't always know about at the time. Remember that learning happens on different days and in different ways for people of all ages."

Suzy interrupts this time. "Okay, that's probably enough teacher talk for the day. I'm going to get dessert. It will take a few minutes, but will be worth the wait."

Nathaniel and I sit at the table with full stomachs and enjoy the warmth of the sunshine and he begins to tell me about how they settled on this house and how he feels about the various neighbors that live up down the road. It sounds like an interesting group of people. They all have a story. After about ten or fifteen minutes, Suzy comes back out with a plate full of churros, a classic Mexican dessert. She evidently just fried them because they are piping hot and covered in cinnamon. Wide-eyed, I say, "Those look and smell amazing. Did you just make them?"

Suzy smiles, "I learned how to make them several years ago and look for every reason to make them when I can. You coming over today was a great reason! Hope you enjoy them."

The first bite melts in my mouth and I get lost in the moment. Before I know it, I've finished the first one and am eyeing a second. However, I restrain myself and decline a second. Don't want to be seen as a chow hound at my first meal with them. But wow, those things are amazing.

We sit and talk about nothing in particular for the next few minutes and finally I say, "I better get going. I have lots of papers to grade and I want to get to some of them today so I won't be grading all afternoon and evening tomorrow. I had such a great time. The food and conversation were amazing. I want to help clear the table and clean the kitchen. What can I do?"

Suzy puts her hand on top of mine and says, "Nathaniel and I have this. We enjoy cleaning up together, don't we Nathaniel?"

Smirking, Nathaniel responds, "Yes, of course, dear. Let me walk you to your car, Meghan."

We walk to the car and I tell him how much fun I had and how I appreciate him inviting me. He opens the door for me and we say goodbye.

My heart is full as I drive away. I just spent a couple of hours with two great people who also happen to be great teachers. They seem happy and have created a great life together. I hope I can find that someday myself. I have a newfound respect for elementary and middle school teachers. Not that I didn't already respect what they do, I just feel I have better insight into how they operate. I know I need to make sure I act more like an elementary teacher when it comes to how I approach teaching, relationships with my students and collaboration with fellow teachers. I want to be more like spaghetti than a waffle.

Nathaniel

As I head back to help Suzy clean up, I can't help but smile. I am glad Meghan came over today. It was important the two of them met and I knew they would hit it off just fine. As I bring dishes to the kitchen, Suzy is already loading the dishwasher and says, "She's a great kid. I like her and can tell why you enjoy spending time with her. You are both lucky. You are a good mentor and she is an eager student."

"Absolutely," I reply enthusiastically. "The kid is definitely a teacher now. She's a few months in and discovering there will be many obstacles for her to overcome. I hope she realizes how easy it might be for her to stay in this place where she is starting to get comfortable. As you know, many teachers never really move past that place where you start to figure a few things out and become complacent. She has so much potential and passion for the kids and teaching. I don't want the bumps in the road to discourage her too much. I'm going to do my best to challenge her to continue to grow and become a good teacher."

Wiping the counter, Suzy says, "We seem to lose at least one young teacher every few years or so. It's a shame they come in so excited and never really get to that place where they are figuring it out and it starts to get easier. She is so lucky to have you to guide her in her journey, and I think she realizes that very few of us get this opportunity."

"I think she knows," I reply. "She's a sponge. She is observant and so inquisitive. I'm not sure I would have known the right questions to ask if I actually did have a mentor when I first started."

At that point I notice Suzy looks like she's really tired. I ask, "You feeling okay? You look tired."

"I'm fine," Suzy replies. "It was a crazy week, and I think I'm just wiped out. I slept in until almost 9:00 this morning. I don't remember the last time I did that. Guess I needed it. And, it was pretty warm out in the garden this morning before I started making lunch."

"You have to take better care of yourself," I say as I wrap her in a hug. "I think I remember you telling me that many times over the years. Looking forward to dinner at Sam's Place tonight."

Suzy smiles and winks, "Me too."

CHAPTER 8

Fly Fishing as a Metaphor for Great Teaching

Nathaniel

The weatherman was right. I could feel the wind blowing the trailer a bit as I drove to the Laguna this morning. The wind is even stronger here. No way will we be able to cast our lines like we want.

The sky is grey and gloomy-looking. It's supposed to be stormy all morning and then clear up this afternoon. Sometimes these storms blow through faster than everyone thinks. I don't think we should chance it and get stuck out there in a storm. I'm not even going to pull over to the ramp. I'm going to wait until she gets here and we can talk about what to do. I probably should've called and canceled last night. Guess I was hoping the forecast would be wrong.

Meghan arrives, gets out of her car and begins to walk to my truck where I'm sitting. It's obvious right away; she didn't look at the forecast. She isn't dressed appropriately for this weather. She gets in the passenger side. I smile and say, "Good morning. How are you?"

"I'm good," she replies. "Definitely not prepared for the weather. I didn't even think to look at the forecast. I was in bed by 8:00 last night. I was tired. But I've been looking forward to today. Even though we didn't have much luck, I had such a great time last time and loved meeting Suzy. I keep thinking about all of the fish we caught on our first trip and still can't get over how big these fish are. And, we're able to catch them in such shallow water. Amazing!"

I look around skeptically. "Well, this wind might wreak havoc on us. The forecast is calling for stormy weather all morning and maybe into the afternoon. I thought about calling you last night and canceling, but thought we could give it a shot. I'm thinking now we should give it a little time and see what happens. Are you up for some breakfast? We could go to Maria's down the road. It's a little cafe and they have a great breakfast menu and we could talk there for a while and see what happens with the weather. What do you think?"

Smiling, Meghan replies, "Great. I'm hungry and always up for a good breakfast."

I assure Meghan her car will be fine here and she can ride with me. "You'll like this place," I say.

We drive a couple miles down the road and arrive at Maria's. We pull into the gravel parking lot and there are only pickup trucks lined up in front. Looks like it's crowded, but that's not surprising. It's crowded every time I come here. Maria's is one of those places that people refer to as a "hole in the wall." The sign across the top that says *Maria's Place* is hand drawn and in need of a fresh coat of paint as the salt water air has taken its toll.

As we walk inside and wait for Maria to come seat us, Meghan says, "This reminds me of a cafe that was in the lodge next to our house in Alaska. Granted, it doesn't have a moose head on the wall. But the tile floor, the low ceiling, and the bar stools look exactly the same. I loved that place. If this is anywhere near as good, I'm gonna love it."

Maria greets us, "*Buenos Dias*."

In my poor attempt at Spanish, I reply, "*Buenos días, Señora. Como esta*?"

Maria responds, "*Muy bien, gracias. Dos para desayuno*?"

I say "*Si*," and she takes us to a small booth towards the back.

The booth seats are covered in red vinyl and the table top is Formica. She hands us a couple of menus and the busboy is right behind her with two glasses of water.

Meghan asks, "What did she ask you before she brought us back here?"

"She asked if it was two for breakfast and I replied yes."

"Impressive," Meghan says. "It's on my bucket list to learn Spanish. Maybe someday."

"My Spanish isn't great," I assure her, "but I do know enough to converse and get by. When Ryan was growing up, he and I used to come here all the time after our fishing trips. He loves this place, and we still come here every time he comes home and we are able to get away to fish. We always get the same thing. Their *huevos rancheros* are amazing. The salsa they put on them is homemade and I don't know how they season their beans, but they are like nothing I've ever had. I've asked many times, but they won't give up the secret. That's what I'm having."

"I've actually never had *huevos rancheros*. What are they?"

Sheepishly, I reply, "Guess, it might help if I explained what they are before I try to sell you on them. They are fried eggs on corn tortillas that are lightly fried and served with salsa and guacamole on top. They also come with refried beans and Mexican rice. They are really good."

Smiling, Meghan says, "Sounds good to me."

Maria arrives at our table with pad and pen in hand ready to take our order. Before she can ask what we want, I say, "Maria, *dos huevos rancheros, por favor.* This rookie here is in for a treat."

Without saying anything, she smiles as if she is laughing at my feeble attempt at Spanish. She then asks, "*¿Le gustaría un café?*"

Meghan smiles and quickly says, "I heard coffee in there somewhere. I would love a cup."

I look at Maria and reply, "*Dos, por favor.*"

Maria winks. Then she takes our menus and walks to the counter.

I chuckle and turn my attention to Meghan. "So, tell me what you have been noticing and wondering at school since we last went fishing."

"It's been another crazy week," Meghan says.

She continues, "I know you said it will get easier, and last time we met, you talked about that season where you become a little more stabilized. I'm holding out hope that I will get there at some point. As you suggested, I've been trying to observe other teachers whenever I can. You know, the 'noticings' and the 'wonderings.' I pay attention to what people say in the teachers' lounge and in the hallways. It's very interesting to see how differently everyone approaches the day-to-day occurrences that arise. I have to tell you, I can see that a few of our colleagues seem to have it figured out. Two that stand out are Jamal in Biology and Danielle in Special Education. When did you guys really start to figure all of it out and become the teachers you seem to be today?"

The busboy brings our coffee. I notice Meghan uses cream and sugar. I'm thinking she's had a few Starbucks coffees in her day. I'm sure she misses luxuries like that, but I haven't heard her complain even on the boat where the only option has been black coffee. I respect that about her.

"It's interesting that you chose those two teachers," I reply. "What is it about them that separates them from the others?"

"Well," Meghan responds, "they both seem to be in a good mood most days. They walk around with a smile on their faces all the time. They seem to know every kid in the school by name. Not just the kids in their classes, but everyone. It would be easy for both of them to just focus on the kids in their classes, but they make a point to connect with all of them. They also call them by their first names rather than their last names. They often ask the kids about their lives outside of school or a class they might be struggling with in school. They've asked me several times how I was doing and told me if I ever needed any help, to let them know. They seem to genuinely care about the students and other teachers. I am amazed and often find myself wondering how they do it.

"As you know, Danielle is with me each day during my 3rd period English 9 class. She is there primarily for two students, Javi and Amber. It didn't take me long to see that Danielle was a great teacher because of the way she interacted with them and the other students in the class. I've learned that Javi is a high functioning student on the autism spectrum. I wouldn't have known that by looking at him. He looks like the other kids, dresses like the other kids and is unassuming. But he *is* quirky. He doesn't pick up on social cues with other kids in social situations and is focused on memorizing sports trivia and information. He is preoccupied with anything sports related and will randomly ask people sport questions.

"Initially, his behavior was disrupting our classroom. It only took Danielle about a week to figure out what needed to happen with Javi. By that time, my eyes were wide open to his differences. Danielle developed a visual schedule and put it on his desk. It was a schedule of the 50-minute class period. She implemented a four-minute time period at the end of class that she called 'sports talk.' During that four-minute period, Javi is allowed to ask a sports-related question of one student or teacher within the classroom. She talked to everyone about what she was doing with Javi and we were all okay with it. Danielle let Javi know that the person he asks may not know the answer and he needs to be okay with that. He has four minutes to discuss with that person what he knows on the subject, regardless of whether the person being asked knows anything on the subject. Once Javi hears his four-minute timer go off, he knows his 'sports talk' time is over and must prepare to transition to his next class.

"Danielle explained to me that if he follows directions throughout the schedule until his 'sports talk' time, he will have opportunities to interact, be accepted, and talk about sports. If he does well for the week, Danielle rewards him with time to get on the ESPN website and print recent articles of interest to him. He likes to memorize. He remembers everything when it comes to sports. It has worked amazingly well, in part because the other students have been willing to participate. Javi bought into the structure and reward system and has been a great student."

At this time our breakfast arrives. The plates are huge, and I can tell by the look on Meghan's face that she didn't expect this much food. Maria warns us the plates are hot and to be careful not to touch them. She lets us know about all of the sauces at the table and variations in extra spice they will add to our dishes. None of the four small bottles have labels on them. Maria tells us they are made from scratch in the kitchen. I smile as I know how good this is all going to taste. I grab the hot sauce bottle she labeled as medium spicy. Meghan elects to go with salt and pepper for her added spice and we both begin to eat.

As we begin to eat, I am thinking about Javi and realize I know about him, but haven't met him yet. After a couple bites and silence at the table, I say, "I think Javi would be a great manager on the football, basketball, or baseball team. He seems to be a coach's dream. You should ask him if he might be interested, and I can talk to the coaches and see what they think."

Taking a sip of coffee, Meghan replies, "That's a great idea. I think he would really like that, and I'll talk to him about it on Monday. By the way, this food is amazing. I can honestly say I've never had eggs like *this* before."

Meghan continues, "The other student, Amber, is emotionally challenged. She is very smart but struggles emotionally and behaviorally. She can be a real stinker at times. Danielle knew right away that we should have some fun, team-building activities the first few days of class to help her feel accepted, part of the group, befriended, and ultimately 'normal.'

"I'm truly amazed at the kind, respectful, caring, consistent, dignified, and loving interactions Danielle has with these students. Rather than speaking loudly for the entire class to hear, Danielle will bend down to discuss an issue she sees starting to brew. And she treats all of the students in the class in much the same way. I think it teaches the rest of the kids in the class that we are all the same in many ways and deserve to be treated with respect. Even when her student is struggling, she remains calm and gives them choices. If needed, she will remove the student in a respectful manner. She will remove the student without looking at me as though she is disgusted and frustrated. She simply removes the student without making a scene.

"One more aspect of teaching that I'm not sure I would have considered if it weren't for Danielle discussing it with me is that quality is often more appropriate than quantity. If the general education students are writing an eight-page paper, it's okay to have Javi and Amber write a two-page paper. Another example is if the general education students are diagramming twenty sentences, cut the paper in half and allow Javi and Amber to diagram ten. They will get the concept, without becoming frustrated. I am learning that is okay. As Danielle says, 'You have to choose your battles and trust that quality teaching is still occurring.' I am so thankful that she is in my class five times a week. I know I am going to continue to learn from her. Our students are so lucky to have her as a teacher."

"How about Jamal?" I ask Meghan.

"I don't get to observe Jamal in the classroom like I do Danielle," she replies, "but I happen to have a few students who are also in Jamal's classes. I asked several of them to describe him as a teacher. As you said in one of our earlier conversations, when I asked them the question, they all said 'I like Mr. Wilson.' They didn't say, 'I respect Mr. Wilson.' As you indicated, they really don't seem to have the ability at their age to distinguish between like and respect. Anyway, each of the students described him as caring, knowledgeable, patient, understanding, willing to provide extra help, and consistently in a positive mood each day. Jamal appears to be very similar to Danielle.

"Finally, the last trait I have noticed about them is that I never hear them join in on the gossip that often happens in the lounge. I don't hear them bad-mouthing other teachers or the administrators. They do talk about the students, but they try to put a positive spin on the situation. They seem so much more mature and optimistic than some of our veteran teachers who have been doing this for much longer."

I notice Meghan's plate has much more food than mine. I've been eating and nodding my head while she talks. Guess I should let her eat before it gets too cold.

"Great observations on your part," I say. "Jamal and Danielle are clearly two of our best teachers. If it will make you feel any better, they have both been right where you are now. It doesn't surprise me that you have noticed they are different. I like to say they are 'cancer-free' when it comes to the negativity that occurs among teachers. They have inoculated themselves from the cynicism and toxic attitudes that often take over a culture within the faculty. You need to know there will be colleagues who will want to 'infect' you during your career. They will attempt to get you to complain about students, teaching conditions, the administration, and a myriad of other factors they feel undermine their enjoyment and success as a teacher. You have to rise above that and just know that mentality ultimately only hurts you and your students. Stay above the fray and take the high road as much as you can.

"I would also tell you that it's rare that a young teacher has the opportunity to observe such an outstanding teacher on a daily basis. As we have discussed and you have probably observed by now, we tend to operate in silos, and the only people who really observe us are our students and occasionally administrators. You are way ahead of the game and fortunate to have such a great teacher to observe and learn from daily. Danielle is an outstanding mentor.

"As you are starting to learn, I have also discovered that not every teacher reaches or spends much time in that season where they are transformational in a positive way with their teaching and the relationships they have with their students. It is our true North. It is the season that we should all be mindful of and working towards. It isn't necessarily a final destination, but it is a place where we have the most potential for truly making a difference in the lives of our students and the colleagues that work with us. Have you heard the terms transactional and transformational leadership?"

Meghan nods between bites of her food. "I have heard of them, but to be honest, don't know that much about them. My dad has mentioned them before based on his experiences in the military."

I smile and say, "It's okay that you don't know that much about them. I would venture to say most people your age don't think about different leadership styles very much. The long and short of it is that transactional leaders are in it for themselves and tend to have only superficial relationships with those around them, while transformational leaders genuinely care about those around them and are more like servant leaders. I would say transformational leaders take the approach that their purpose is to serve their subordinates and help them achieve their goals, as opposed to the transactional approach where the subordinates are supposed to serve the leader and make him or her look good. Transactional leaders care very little about developing meaningful relationships with those around them. It is simply about the bottom line. They prefer to operate in a one-way communication system where the leader gives an order and the subordinate executes the order. The two people involved don't really need to know much about each other and certainly don't have to care about the other."

Meghan smiles and says, "It's obvious which one I would like to adopt."

"I'm right there with you," I say. "I think it's the same with most teachers and I truly believe most of us get into the profession because we want to make a difference in the lives of students. Most of us had a teacher along the way who made a difference for us, and we say we want to be like them. However, we find out it is much harder than we thought to be that teacher. You have to figure out who you are, what you value, and what it means to teach in a way that is meaningful before you have any chance of being a teacher who has transformational relationships.

"Remember Dana, the teacher who I said was such a positive influence early in my career?"

"I do," Meghan replies. "She seemed to have really made an impact on you."

"Yes, she did," I continue. "I was contrasting her influence with Jim Tingle, the cynical department chair. One of the most important pieces of advice Dana gave me was that I needed to discover who I was as a teacher. What did I value? What did I believe about teaching methods? What did I believe about curriculum design? What did I believe about the type of experience students should have in my classroom? And I learned, sometimes the hard way, what I needed to in order to become a teacher.

"I learned about child development by entering into the lives of my students and watching them grow over the course of several years. I learned about teaching methods by experimenting with those methods that I had been taught, assessing their effectiveness, engaging in professional development opportunities to learn more, and creating my own. I learned how to write a perfect lesson plan by throwing out almost everything I had been taught regarding the perfect lesson plan. I realized such a lesson plan doesn't exist . . . only the perfect learning environment. In fact, I learned early on that it made no sense for me to get to the end of my perfect lesson plan if I left my students behind ten minutes into the lesson. What good was it if I completed my lesson plan yet they learned nothing? I had been trained to devote a certain number of minutes to each section of my lesson plan. However, I realized through time that minutes aren't magic. Minutes do not equal learning. Teaching has nothing to do with minutes expired in talking at kids. Rather it has everything to do with facilitating learning with kids regardless of the number of minutes provided.

"I also eventually learned about curriculum design. I learned that curriculum design is less about what others say it is and how it should be taught, and more about how I see the content and how I think it should be packaged and delivered. This all involves understanding what you, as the teacher, value. This is known as teacher value orientations. I never really thought about this concept until I attended a professional conference about 20 years ago where this concept was just beginning to be discussed. I listened to a teacher education researcher discuss various belief systems and value orientations that most teachers possess, and for the first time in my career, I felt validated. I learned the best way for us to teach is through our values and beliefs. I learned that caring for kids, loving them when they are unlovable, and cherishing the creation of caring relationships with my students was not only okay, it was essential if I was going to be authentic as their teacher.

"This was a huge light bulb moment for me! Even though I'd been teaching for five to six years, and was fairly effective and well-liked most of the time, I still had a little voice in the back of my head telling me there was something wrong with me. I valued students' experiences in my class and having the ability to create a sense of balance in my classroom. Like many of my peers at the time, I had been taught that content was the most important focus. Our job as teachers was to deliver the content to students. And while I don't necessarily disagree with this, I never really valued that as the most important part of my job. Don't get me wrong, there are those teachers who do value the content as the most important part of their job, and they are very good and effective teachers who make a significant impact in the lives of their students. Although counter-intuitive, there is one significant quality that we share in common. If you teach through your values, being true to yourself as a teacher, you will find teaching methods and curricular models that complement your values. And, bottom line, kids will learn. You will be effective as a teacher, and you will be authentic.

"This was absolutely a game-changer for me in my development as a teacher. Until that time, I was trying to be the type of teacher I thought I was supposed to be. Then I realized I needed to be the type of teacher I was 'wired' to be. Once I realized this, there was no stopping me. I felt empowered to be me, my authentic self as a teacher, and to use my gifts and talents to absolutely maximize my performance in the classroom and that of my students.

"Many novice teachers start out as transactional teachers. It's all about them, their ego, their success if students learn, and their ability to manage. I could go on. But something dramatic and fairly subtle occurs as they journey through becoming a teacher who makes a difference in students' lives. For some, this occurs over the course of years, and for others, it may occur more rapidly. But, it seems for all of them, there are some qualities that they have in common.

"Let me sum it up, and I'll explain a bit more in detail. If a teacher is truly one who is transformational, she will have what I would call an ethic of care. She cares about kids, teachers, her school, her community, the profession, methods, and curricula. Having an ethic of care simply means that *caring* is the same as *being* for those teachers. Caring is not something that they can switch on and off. Caring is not something that they do. Rather it is who they are. They teach through caring relationships they form with their students. Essentially, these teachers believe if they can get the students into the palm of their hands relationally, they can teach them anything. It is relationship first. I've had some teachers who were like that and then others who were not. That is one of the differences between transactional and transformational."

"That sounds great," Meghan says to me, "but how do teachers who have this way of caring become that way? I mean, are they just born that way? Or is this something they learn somewhere along the way? Because that truly is the kind of teacher that I want to be. But there are times when I don't feel like I really do care about some of these kids. To be honest, Nathaniel, I'm ashamed to say I've already had a few moments of wondering if teaching is what I am supposed to be doing. Of course, those moments come at the end of a tough day and I'm tired, or they occur after a particular encounter with a student when I think, 'I'll never reach that one, and frankly I don't care!' I don't want to have those thoughts. How do I think about it differently?"

"So I have another question for you," I say. "Have you ever seen the movie *A River Runs Through It*?"

"Sure. Actually, my entire family has seen it."

Maria comes back to the table, remarks how clean our plates are and asks if we are finished. Refraining from any further mangling of the Spanish language, I simply smile and reply, "Yes, it was amazing."

Meghan smiles, rubs her stomach and says, "I truly loved every bite of it and will bring my parents here when they visit."

"I look forward to meeting them," Maria says. "More coffee or water?"

I look at Meghan and she raises her hand and waves me off as if to say no. I say to Maria, "I would like a little more coffee please. We would also like to hang out a bit, talk some more and see if the weather passes, if that's okay."

"Of course. Stay as long as you like."

I look back at Meghan, "Getting back to the movie, remember, it was set in Montana and based on the true story about a family where fly fishing is basically the metaphor for life. There were two sons in the story, and both were passionate fishermen who had been taught by their dad. There are incredible scenes in the movie of the boys and their dad fly fishing in these magnificent rivers that run through Montana. I can imagine it was much like some of the streams and rivers you fished in as a kid in Alaska. It's one of my favorite movies. I've probably watched it a dozen times by now, yet every time I watch it, I am struck by the fishing scenes. Not only the beauty and artistry of the craft of fly fishing and the splendid majesty of nature, but as a teacher, I am a fly fisherman. Every day, my job as a teacher is to find a way to get the students into the palm of my hand. If I succeed, they learn and I enjoy teaching. If I fail, they don't learn as well, and I struggle in my teaching. So, how do you fly fish? What did you and those boys and their dad in Montana do to catch those beautiful fish?"

Meghan thinks for a moment before replying. "I guess first you've got to know where to find the fish. You have to read the water."

"Yep, and where do you find the fish you are teaching?" I ask. "How do you read the water?"

Smiling, Meghan replies, "I guess my students are the fish. I mean, they walk into my room and sit down. It's more like a fishbowl than a raging river."

"Yes, but are they all the same? Aren't some of the fish in your classroom hiding in the shadows trying not to be seen, while others are rising to the surface hanging on every word you are saying? It's almost like you don't even have to try with those fish. They literally sometimes just jump into your net. You've snagged them and it's easy. The real test is to get those that don't want to be caught into the palm of your hand. You've read the water and you know where the fish are hiding. What does the fisherman need to do next?"

Meghan's eyes have come alive with recognition. "He has to find the right fly to cast into the water. He has to know what bugs or flies the fish will respond to and want to eat. That's called the hatch."

Reaching across the table and giving Meghan a fist bump, I say, "You do know how to fish! And once the fisherman knows what that fly or bug looks like, he spends time making a replica. When finished, he ties it to the end of his fishing line, casts it into the water, and waits to see if there is a response from the fish. As you can probably appreciate, I think the act of tying the fly and casting the line is a thing of beauty. The fisherman now has something in common with the fish. The fish want a certain fly and the fisherman has it. You know, finding common interests you have with your students is a great first step to developing a relationship with them so that they feel you care. OK, let's say you do all that. You know the fly needed, you cast it out beautifully, and the fish does not respond. It just lays there uninterested in what you have to offer it. What does the fisherman do next?"

"Well, you mean, besides getting frustrated and giving up?" Meghan asks.

"Yes, besides that," I say with a chuckle.

Continuing, Meghan says, "This makes me think of a student earlier this week who just sat there unresponsive in class and just stared blankly into space. I guess she was my uninterested fish. I guess I didn't have the right fly. I didn't even try to find out what we might have in common. I just really kind of gave up on her. That would be the same as that fisherman packing up and going home because the first guess at the fly was unsuccessful. If the fisherman really wants to catch that fish, he reels his line back in and replaces the first fly with another one and tries again. And if that doesn't work, he continues, trying to find out what that fish wants or needs."

"Exactly!" I respond. "Teaching is exactly like fly fishing. A relationship must be formed between students and teachers where they are understood. So, let's play this out a bit further. Let's say that finally, the fisherman has the correct fly, casts it into the shadows, and the fish rises and bites the fly, becoming hooked. Is the fisherman done? Is he successful yet?"

Thinking for a brief moment, Meghan replies, "I guess he may feel successful. He's got a fish on the line. But I remember that scene in *A River Runs Through It* where one of the brothers finally has a fish on his line and, when reeling him in, the fish jumps the hook. It gets away. That has happened to me many times as well. There is definitely something to the art of reeling in the fish."

"Yes," I say, "It's not enough to simply catch a fish. The art is in reeling it into the palm of your hand. You have to reel it into your net. And this is done subtly and carefully. It's not rushed. The fish may take off and run with the hook in his mouth and the fisherman has to let him go and bide his time and yet continue to gradually reel him in. And when he finally gets close enough, the fish is gently netted. Then and only then have you caught a fish.

I take another sip of coffee and feel the caffeine working its magic. "The next decision of what to do with the fish is also an interesting one. For some, the fish will be a meal, while for others the fish will be caught and then released to return to water. But regardless of what happens next, the beauty of fly fishing is finding what you have in common and gently reeling the fish into the palm of your hand. Fly fishing, whether for fish or for your students, is both an art and a science.

"I should also point out that you can fish with dynamite. You can take a stick of dynamite and you can hurl it in the vicinity of where you think the fish may be, and it will explode, and many fish may die. It's brutal and it's ugly. However, in the end you can still say that you went fishing. The experience and results in this case are certainly not beautiful. Unfortunately, there are teachers who fish with dynamite for their students. They ridicule, humiliate, embarrass, and shame. They blame them for not being the student hanging on every word eager to learn. They shame them for hiding in the shadows of a classroom environment. And they cause destruction in the lives of students who they otherwise could rescue simply because they do not care enough to do the work necessary to find the right 'fly' and learn more about both the art and science of reeling them into the palm of their hands."

Meghan gives me a wide smile. "Wow! I have never thought about it like that. I had some thoughts in my head this past week that thankfully I didn't say out loud. If I'd allowed myself to speak them, I surely would have been fishing with dynamite. Thanks for helping me to understand this. And now, every time we are fishing, I will remember this discussion."

Looking outside, I say, "I'm glad that analogy resonated with you. It certainly does for me. Looks like the weather isn't going to break. We'll have to just chalk this fishing trip up as a good conversation over great food. I need to head back home. Suzy needs help with a few things, and I want to make sure I'm there to help her."

"Oh sure," Meghan replies. "Let's go. This place is unbelievable! I will definitely be bringing my mom and dad here when they come to town. They love small places like this off the beaten path. They'll love the food, and I think they will get a kick out of how much it looks like the cafe in Alaska where we used to eat."

We both stand up to leave. "I'd like to continue this next time we meet, if that's okay."

"Definitely," Meghan says. "This seems really important. I have so many questions, and I know I will have more."

"Sure thing," I reply. "I could talk about this stuff anytime. I look forward to it."

Meghan

What a great breakfast. I ate too much, but that's okay. I can't wait to take Mom and Dad there. WOW! FLY FISHING! Well that's what we've been doing all along. I wonder if he knew we'd be having this conversation at some point. Forming relationships, whether with students or with fish, is exactly the same process. Who knew? So many lessons from Nathaniel today. Let's see . . . what are the nuggets from today? OK . . . I need to revisit my philosophy on what I value, what I believe about teaching methods and curriculum design. What type of experience do I want the students in my classroom to have?

Nathaniel talked about transactional and transformational. Yes, work on being transformational. Funny how Dad has talked to me about it before, and I definitely listened to him. It seems somehow different coming from Nathaniel. It's probably because I'm more mature and ready to hear the message.

I didn't think about it, but I know I am lucky to observe Danielle and Jamal. They are what I want to be when I grow up as a teacher. It seems that if you ask any teacher, she would say she wants to be transformational. It's hard to see why we wouldn't always be striving to be that teacher.

There was so much rich information today. I know I am going to reflect on this for a while. I only hope I can become the type of teacher he was describing. Can I ever get to that place? Some days I think yes, and others there is no way I will ever get there. I know it's a journey, but it feels pretty daunting. I'm sure glad Nathaniel is there to answer my questions. I know most of the other first year teachers could only wish to have someone like him to mentor them.

EXIT SLIP NUMBER THREE

1. *Fly fishing is a great analogy for how great teachers teach.*
2. *Relationships come before the learning.*
3. *I want to be that teacher who knows just the right bait to catch the kids . . . even the ones that are tough to reach.*

Nathaniel

After my normal routine of putting the boat away, I enter the back door and walk through the house. I find Suzy at the desk in our home office taking care of some paperwork. She looks up and turns towards me as I get to the doorway.

"Hey there. Having a good morning?" I ask.

"Yes, it's been a good morning. I haven't gotten much done around here, but it's been relaxing. How is Meghan? Did you guys get to fish today? It's been raining and stormy here all morning."

"We didn't fish this morning and that's okay. We went to Maria's for breakfast, and I introduced to her to their *huevos rancheros*. She was blown away. They definitely have a new customer. We sat there and talked for a good while and focused on what it means to be a great teacher. We talked about those traits that separate those great teachers from the rest. I shared with her the analogy that great teaching is much like fly fishing. I've been thinking about that for a while and was looking for a way to make it real for her. I think she got it. I was making much of it up as I went. But I think it was pretty good."

"I haven't really heard you use that analogy before. What do you mean teaching is like fly fishing?" Suzy asks.

"Essentially, great teachers, like great fishermen, know which 'bait' to use when trying to catch fish. The great teachers realize they can't use the same bait every day, and not every student is eager to take the bait and learn. You have to be creative to reach those hanging in the background like some fish hang back in the deeper water. It is an art to catch them, teach them, and then release them."

"It makes a lot of sense," Suzy says with a smile. "I'm sure she got it as well and appreciated the analogy, since she likes to fish. Can we just hang out here for a little while? I know you aren't hungry, but I could use a little something to eat. Would you make something simple for me?"

"Sure," I reply. "What would you like?

CHAPTER 9

Theories and Truth

Meghan

I can't believe how hard I slept last night. It seems I'm always exhausted by Friday night. For a very brief moment, it was tempting to push snooze on the alarm this morning. But as soon as I remembered I was going fishing in such a beautiful place, I was up and moving. It's foggy as I am driving this morning. The sun isn't up yet and I know the fog will lift because I actually checked the weather forecast this time. It's going to be a beautiful day. I wonder if I'll beat Nathaniel there this morning.

As always, he's here and ready to launch the boat. He must get up at 4 AM to get here before me. He gets out of his truck as I pull up next to him. He's smiling as he begins loading the fishing equipment onto the boat.

"What a beautiful morning," I say as I approach.

"It sure is," Nathaniel replies. "I like it when it's foggy like this early and then burns off as the sun rises. We're going to have a great day on the water."

"I like the fog as well," I say. "I have to tell you, I was sleeping hard when that alarm went off this morning. My friends still can't believe that I get up so early to go fishing on a Saturday morning. I tell them I love it, and the Saturday afternoon nap helps . . . a bunch."

Nathaniel smiles. "That's funny. I take those Saturday afternoon naps too. Nothing like it. I've heard the fish have been feeding like crazy lately. I bet we see lots of reds with their tails in the air. Love that sight. Let's get this boat launched. It's going to be great out there today. I can feel it."

As Nathaniel drives the boat slowly away from the dock, I say, "You know, your analogy of fly fishing and teaching has stuck with me. I watched the movie *A River Runs Through It* again that next week and was actually mesmerized by the fly fishing scenes. I've thought much more about my own fly fishing abilities the last few weeks. I've tried to focus on all of my students, even those 'hiding in the shadows.' I'm working hard to find something I might have in common with some of my students. And, I'm beginning to have a tiny bit of success."

The fog begins to lift as Nathaniel's boat skims across the water.

"Remember Lisa?" I ask.

"She's the one you mentioned the last time we were together. Right?"

"Yes," I reply. "She came in yesterday and sat in her chair, oblivious, like she always does, seemingly disinterested and not caring. I thought, today I'm going to try to connect with her. I'm going to see if we can find something in common other than the fact that we have to endure the same time each day together. So when she came in, I intentionally looked at her to see what I could notice about her. I don't think she likes me or my class, so I have probably avoided really seeing her. Was anything different today? And you know what, the first thing I noticed is that she had changed her hair color. I'm not even sure what color it was before. Some mousy brown I think. How bad is that? I can't even remember. But today, I noticed that her hair was now red. And it struck me that this could very well be the thing that I have needed to connect with her.

"So as she walked toward her desk and settled in while others were still coming into the room, I approached her and said, 'Hi, Lisa. How are you today? You have changed your hair! That red color looks good on you!' And to my utter surprise, she replied, 'Thanks. I like the color of your hair and thought I'd see what I looked like with the same color.' And in that moment I realized this was her way of trying to connect with me. I hadn't even been aware that she noticed me or connected to me in any way. Apparently, she did. I was stunned, to say the least. I said, 'Thanks, I had no idea.' And then she smiled. It was time to get class started.

"As I walked to the front of the class, goosebumps flooded up and down my body and I felt tears welling up. As I turned to face the class, another student, Julio, who is one of those fish jumping into my net every day, sitting in the front row, saw the expression on my face and the trace of tears in my eyes, and mouthed 'Are you OK?' I nodded at him, broke into a wide smile, and I was full and overflowing."

Nathaniel smiles knowingly. "I love that you are growing and learning. And yes, this teaching gig is full of emotion. You had an emotional response to Lisa's response yesterday. *Full and overflowing*. Sounds like it's been a good few weeks for you."

"It's been a good week," I say with a smile. "I have been reflecting so much about not only fly fishing, but also about what you said about transformational teachers being those that have an ethic of care. Can you explain that a little more?"

"Yes," Nathaniel replies. "I have lots more to say about that. Let's get to our fishing spot and we can talk more about it."

He then increases speed and I turn and feel that familiar wind in my face and smile as I take in a deep breath of the salt air. It is fall now and the air is a bit cooler, but not much. It is definitely different than back home. I could sit here and take this in for a while.

We finally arrive in an area we haven't gone before. Nathaniel shuts down the motor and he gets the pole and starts to push us along. The water we are in can't be more than eight to ten inches deep. It's crazy how shallow the water is and the size of the fish that we are able to catch. The water is crystal clear and it looks like our boat is floating on glass. The water is completely still and the fog is beginning to lift. The scene is simply breathtaking. I smile and take it all in.

As he is standing on the platform and pushing us along quietly, he continues our conversation. "You know, actually understanding how to form caring relationships where we can teach others is a fairly simple formula. Scholars have written about this topic for some time. Yet, as human beings, we still struggle to do this well.

"So here goes. I'm going to illustrate this by using ideas put forth by one of my favorites, Nel Noddings. She was a researcher who studied how to build caring relationships over 30 years ago. She suggested that in every relationship there are two people. And that each of those people has a role to either be the one caring or the one cared-for. In fact, that's what she called the roles.

"So, in our case, we, as teachers, are in the caring role and our students are in the cared-for roles. There are basically three things that the one caring must do in her role. She must first be willing to see the world through the eyes of the cared-for. Noddings referred to this as engrossment. In other words, for teachers, this is having the willingness to understand what the world is like for her students. What is their life like? What is their perspective? What is their learning experience? Without knowing this, the teacher is unable to truly understand her student.

"Second, the teacher must commit to being there for her students. She can't say 'I'm not committed.' The students need to know that you are committed to them, to their learning, and to them being their best self.

"Third, Noddings suggested that, if teachers are truly caring, they will have experienced what she called the motivational shift. This one is difficult to understand. The motivational shift is about our motivation as teachers. What gets us out of bed and to work? The motivational shift occurs when our motivation is less about what we do and more about what students learn. It is less about our teaching and more about their experience learning. It is less about us and our success and more about them and their success. In other words, our motivation has shifted from a focus on ourselves as teachers to a focus on our students as learners. The shift in these three areas is essential if there is to be a relationship of care established with our students."

I sit there for a moment in silence, thinking. I finally say, "I think I get this. But can't a teacher do all of that and never make a significant connection with a student? I mean, I'm really trying and certainly more mindful and intentional in fly fishing and noticing and wondering, and yet, I'm worried that I won't be able to reach them all."

"Yes," Nathaniel replies. "A teacher can be all these and still struggle relationally with some students. BUT—and this is a big BUT—that is typically because the student hasn't demonstrated the two characteristics that are absolutely essential for that relationship of care to be completed. The cared-for has two responsibilities. He has to receive the care and respond to the care. And if those don't happen, no amount of trying on the part of the teacher will ever make a difference.

"It's the fly fishing scenario where you have the right fly tied on, make a beautiful cast into the water, lay it right in front of the fish's nose, and yet it simply doesn't move toward it. The fish doesn't receive it or respond to it regardless of how many times the fisherman tries. We can connect this to what happened with Lisa yesterday. You noticed her hair and commented on it. That was engrossment to her. She received your comment and responded by noting that she liked your red hair. And that emotional response you felt, those goosebumps, and that feeling of being full and overflowing is the motivational shift. I bet when you see her next week you will be eager to make another connection."

I smile and say, "I definitely will."

"So you see, this is how it works," Nathaniel continues. "This is what's necessary to be that transformational teacher and to be a teacher with an ethic of care. It's a continual and ongoing process. We are never finished becoming the teacher that we are purposed to be. But once you discover the formula, it becomes easier to reach your students. Not just those who are easy to catch."

"Wow," I say. "That makes so much sense and seems so doable. Okay, I know I should aspire to be a transformational teacher who possesses an ethic of care. But something else you mentioned in our last meeting has also stuck with me. You said something about balance, and challenges to maintaining balance. Could we talk about that a bit more?"

"Well, this might take me a while to explain," Nathaniel replies. "Let's get out of the boat and catch some of those fish."

We can see fish feeding in the shallow water and I'm excited to see if we can catch a few today. So, we both get ready.

"I don't think I'm going to use waders today," I say. "What do you think about me fishing in my sneakers? They are old and I'm not worried about getting them messy."

Nathaniel laughs. "That's great. I'm right there with you."

With that we both step into water that comes just below my knees and start casting. I lay my line out on the water and within a couple of seconds, I'm reeling one in. We both catch several in the next half hour or so. We are laughing, enjoying the moment and making small talk.

We both sit on the edge of the boat and begin to drink water. "Where were we in our conversation?" Nathaniel asks.

Before I can answer, he says, "Oh yeah, the balance thing. It's something that I've struggled with and tried to figure out for years. So this is what I've come to realize. Over the course of my long career, I've known many teachers. Some are now long gone. Some are retired. Some are still in the trenches with me. Some are young and some are old. Some knew they wanted to teach since childhood and others came into it after another career. Regardless of how I encountered them, they all seemed to share a few characteristics in common.

"First, they all had some early experience in their childhood that led them to believe they were supposed to become a teacher. It may have been a teacher that made them feel special or a teacher they hated who inspired them to be a teacher who didn't make kids feel that way. Or it may have been having caring role models as teachers who modeled what it means to create caring relationships with students. A second characteristic they seemed to have in common beyond role models was when they made the decision to teach. It seems that the earlier teachers make the decision to teach, the more they begin to think of themselves as teachers.

"For example, even as small children, if they identify as a teacher, kids will play school. I've got a four-year-old granddaughter right now who says she wants to grow up to be a teacher. She reminds me of what you were probably like growing up. She takes her dolls and plays school, planning lessons, and writing on a blackboard.

"She may or may not grow up to be a teacher, but if she decides to teach, she will have identified as a teacher for almost 20 years before actually having a job as a teacher. She will watch teachers teach. She will notice how they work with students. She will notice how they organize their classroom. She will notice how they handle everything from an interruption at their doors to a disruption in the classroom. In essence, my granddaughter, should she decide to become a teacher, will start becoming one simply by watching and observing. It is those 'noticings' and 'wonderings' we've talked about. She will not even realize that she is doing this. And should she notice things like her teacher staying at school long after all the other teachers have left or opening up her purse to give a student lunch money when they've forgotten theirs, she will begin to build an ideal of what it means to be a teacher. Does that make sense?"

"Yeah, definitely. I can relate to it. I do think we imitate what we see being modeled for us by someone we respect."

"I believe it happens in many professions," Nathaniel says. "A child becomes interested in something, has an encounter with someone who does it well, and begins to emulate what they see that person doing. A kid goes to the doctor. The doctor is kind, funny, smart, wears a white coat and helps the kid feel better. The kid says, 'When I grow up, I want to be a doctor.' Going forward, every time that kid encounters a doctor, she will be picking up all the cues of behavior of what it means to be one. I think this is particularly true when that teacher that the child is noticing and wondering about is also one that the child loves. That teacher becomes a role model for that child through the caring relationship that has been established. So that's one characteristic I see transformational teachers having in common. They had a caring role model as a teacher in their life.

"Secondly, I've seen something occur in many teachers when they became a parent. It's funny, but when you become a parent, lots of things obviously change. Beyond the diapers, the crying, the sleepless nights, there is also an awareness of how very sacred this little life is and how very responsible you are for it. I didn't realize this at first, of course, but it was about the time that my oldest was three years old and we sent him to a nursery school class that I thought, boy, I hope they take care of him like I would if I was his teacher. Because, you know, I'm his dad, and I couldn't bear to think that a teacher wouldn't have the same best interest of my child as I do.

"I really started analyzing this, and about a week later, still caught up in my own thoughts about it, I walked into my classroom and noticed that one of my 9th grade girls looked like she had been crying. It was the first period of the day, so whatever had gone wrong to cause her to cry had happened either at home or on her way here. I remember thinking, if I were her parent, what would I do? Give her a hug? That might be risky in this day and age. Should I ignore her? Should I ask her if she's OK? And that's when it really dawned on me.

"Up until then, I think I would have ignored her. Oh, I would have seen her, but it would have made me uncomfortable to really try to help her. But at that moment, given my thoughts about my son and nursery school, I felt something change in me. I didn't view her as an objective observer and teacher; I realized that she was someone's child. I had a child and I understood the responsibility of being a parent. And, I never realized before that my child may be sad at school. I began to hope that someone there would see his sadness and do something for him to make him feel better.

"Becoming a dad truly helped me to learn this. I've had this same conversation with other teachers, both those who have children and those without. And quite honestly, those without children were somewhat offended when I suggested that because I'm a parent, I'm a better teacher. Well, even though that's not exactly what I meant, this one teacher, Kahlee Clark, responded by saying, 'Do you mean to say that because I'm not a mom, I can't be a good teacher . . . a teacher who cares?"

Smiling, I say, "I have to admit, I was thinking the same thing. What does that mean for me? Will I not be a good teacher until I become a parent?"

As if he is worried he offended me, Nathaniel quickly says, "No, that's not what I meant at all. The next day, Kahlee saw me in the teachers' lounge and followed up, saying that she'd been thinking about what I'd said the night before and came to her own conclusion about it. She suggested that what it really was about was having the opportunity to practice care for someone to whom we have a responsibility. She went on to explain that, although a fairly new teacher (I think she'd been teaching for about four years), she truly cared for her students and had established very strong trusting relationships with most of them. So what she thought I was really saying about this was that the more we have an opportunity to be caring and practice caring for others, the better we are as teachers.

"I couldn't disagree with her. This did make sense. She explained that, just like I had learned how to practice being a dad with my son, she had learned about caring for others by being a nanny to a family with three kids for three years during college. So, bottom line, it's not being a parent that makes you a more caring teacher. It's about practicing caring for others that you are responsible for, whether it's your own child or someone else's.

"And then something else seems to happen to teachers as they move from that transactional to transformational we talked about before. They begin to receive confirmation that they are worthy as a teacher. Maybe it's a series of teacher evaluations from another teacher or the principal that confirms best practice. Maybe it's when that teacher is asked to work on writing a new curriculum or in solving a school issue. Maybe it's when that teacher receives that note from a former student that says 'Thank you.' Regardless, it seems once these affirmations begin to happen, there is also this realization they are making a difference. This is the confirmation that most of us need. We went into teaching to make a difference.

"So when I talk with teachers who are in this significant season of their life, and hear their teaching journey unfold, somewhere in there is the beginning of a sense of confirmation. They are the teacher who they wanted to be all along. I think some teachers leave the profession if they don't get that confirmation. Others who don't get that confirmation tend to settle and go through the motions. Teaching for them becomes a job and something they do rather than a calling and someone that they are."

I look across the water, and then back at Nathaniel. "So, you are saying that our role models as teachers matter, practicing caring for others matters, and receiving some type of confirmation matters. I can see that, but I want to get you back to my original question today. What about being able to find balance in life?"

"Oh, right!" Nathaniel says. "I told you this would take a while. Here's the deal. Those caring teachers served as positive roles models in so many ways. They also modeled some behaviors that perhaps weren't so positive. In my own 'noticings' and 'wonderings' of teachers and in my own story, some of what was modeled to us was an idea of self-sacrifice. We hear it in sports all the time. Many times there is an expectation that the coach will sacrifice to a point that his health is at risk. I've seen this in teaching over and over again. For example, you know our drama teacher, Rita Mercer? Rita has been one of our teachers for probably fifteen years. At the end of every year, our senior class will put on a musical. Over the years, they've tackled everything from *My Fair Lady* to *Les Miserables* to *A Chorus Line* to *Cabaret* to *West Side Story*. These are really enormous undertakings for any one person to tackle. Rita is simply amazing at this.

"Early in the school year, she organizes interested students. She also begins the work of picking the musical, coordinating with the orchestra, band, and music departments. She enlists the help of the art department, works with the business students in a media campaign and ticket sales, auditions students for the various roles, and casts the parts.

"As if that's not enough, starting in January, Rita will be here before school, after school, in the evenings, and on weekends working with the students in rehearsals. And all of this culminates in May with an extraordinary performance over two weekends. When Rita first got here, she launched this idea at a faculty meeting and most of us thought she was crazy to suggest that our students and our school could actually pull off something of this magnitude. Guess what? With Rita's single-minded dogged determination, optimism and enthusiasm, and seemingly unending supply of energy, she does it every single year.

"Underclassmen at our school look forward to the year when they have the opportunity to be part of this musical production. Over the years the community has also rallied, and these musicals are sold out each and every performance. From all appearances, it would seem like Rita is one of the happiest and most dedicated teachers we have. But, there is always a story. Every teacher has a story. Unfortunately, Rita faced a serious consequence from all of this. You see, Rita's love of theater and her dedication to producing these amazing musical shows was something that her own favorite teacher had modeled to her when she was in high school.

"Rita shared this with me years ago when she first started doing this, and I was skeptical. Rita said she'd always wanted to be like that teacher who turned kids on to drama and theater. As she became better and better as a teacher and journeyed through those early teaching years of uncertainty, she was most affirmed by the success of her students. When she could see her students learning and saw the joy in their eyes as they performed in her plays and musicals, she felt good. She felt good about herself and about her teaching. We have a tendency to continue to do that which makes us feel good. And for Rita, and for many teachers, including myself at times, we will be affirmed more in our work than in any other aspect of our lives."

At this point, Nathaniel begins to get up and says, "I think we should give these fish another run for their money. Want to move to a different spot?"

"Absolutely," I say as I stand up and stretch as well.

Back on the deck of the boat, I ask if I can be the one to push us around using the pole. Nathaniel is happy to oblige and gives me a quick lesson on how to do it. We set out for another good area to fish. It seems even more spectacular from the top of the platform in the back of the boat. We see several fish after a short journey and Nathaniel suggests we try this spot. We get in the water and again, my knees are barely wet. Amazing!

As we begin to cast, Nathaniel continues: "We often hear people say we should have balance in our lives. But for many of us, if we aren't really conscious of what we need to balance, the scales will tip to that which makes us feel most affirmed and most successful. As teachers, I think we have three distinct areas of our lives that we need to balance and care for. We need to care for our students. We need to care for our families, and we need to care for ourselves. The challenge is in maintaining that balance.

"I refer to this as my 'triangle of tension paradox.' Somehow,

I need to put as much purpose and intention into taking care of myself and my family as I do my students. This becomes a challenge for teachers who want to be great at their craft. I would argue that it's very difficult to pursue greatness in something and truly have balance in your life. Think of the best athletes, coaches, doctors, attorneys. You name it. If you are pursuing greatness in something, you are putting an inordinate amount of energy and focus into that endeavor. There is very little time and energy left for other aspects of your life. If I am being affirmed because of what I am achieving in my work with students at school, then my energies will be directed to that end. I will continue to pour more of myself into my work so I will continue to be affirmed. We all love to be affirmed. If this happens, it is very easy to completely lose any sense of balance in our lives at all.

Pausing for a brief moment as if he's a little hesitant to share something, Nathaniel says, "This happened to me about fifteen years ago. I was loving my work, loving my students, enjoying the relationships I had with the staff at school. I was spending all of my time either at school or thinking about school. I was involved in so many ways at school and it felt very good. However, what became clear is I enjoyed being at school more than being home with Suzy and the kids.

"Being at school gave me a sense of accomplishment and affirmation, whereas being at home meant having to deal with my wife's needs for companionship and my kids' needs for spending time with me. Home wasn't as fun. All of this took a huge toll on my marriage. Thankfully, my wife loved me enough to tell me the truth. She's the one who finally figured this out for me. I mean I knew that we were really just going through the motions of being married at the time, and I knew she wasn't happy about it. But honestly, I didn't know what was wrong. I thought things were fine. I eagerly went to work every day excited and came home every night tired but fulfilled because of that affirmation I'd received in teaching.

"One day she told me that we needed to talk. I'm not sure any man wants to hear those words. I knew what was going to come next might be uncomfortable. She simply said, 'Do you love us? Do you love us enough to want to spend time with us? We need you. I want you to be as excited to come home from work to me and the kids as you are to go to work and be with your students. It seems like you can't wait to go to work and you dread coming home. The only topics you ever talk about are what is happening at school. I need more, but I'm not sure you realize it. If this is true, then it's time to decide if we are really going to make it.' I was stunned and sat silently trying to figure out how this could have happened to us. As I looked at the tears in her eyes, it became glaringly obvious to me that she was right. I did like being at school more than being home. I did feel better about myself at school than at home."

I pause from casting and look at Nathaniel as I say, "That must've been hard for both of you . . . all four of you actually. I'm sure it wasn't easy for you to hear. But, good for Suzy that she would say something rather than let it continue to come between you and your family."

Nathaniel nods his head solemnly, deep in thought.

I stare out at the water as I continue speaking: "I know we haven't talked about my relationships, but as you probably know by now, I'm not in a significant relationship. I honestly don't think I would have the time or energy for someone else at this point. But I can see how working to be a great teacher can cause you to neglect other relationships in your life."

Nathaniel chuckles and says, "I wasn't ready for a significant relationship when I was in that first year of teaching either. Going back to what I said a minute ago, our human nature drives us to do whatever makes us feel better at the time. Honestly, I was really oblivious to the effect this was having on my relationships with my family. Although it took us a little while to get back on track, that was the moment that I made a conscious decision to try my best to get balance back into my life. I'm so thankful that my wife loved me enough to tell me the truth and to ask difficult questions of me.

"It didn't turn out so well for Rita. She earned a phenomenal reputation as one of the best teachers this school has ever had, but she lost her own marriage for the same reason I almost lost mine. Rita poured all of herself into her work. Between the hours away from home, her need for affirmation as a teacher, her dedication to achieving something monumental each and every year, and the expectations that she placed upon herself, she simply wasn't there for her husband. He tried. I've met him. He's a great guy. It ultimately just didn't work for them. They divorced after three years of marriage. Thankfully, they didn't have children. It's amazing how predictable this can be when our sense of affirmation comes from something that simply does not include our spouse or significant other.

"I could go on and on about that topic. But, Meghan, here's what I want you to know. Teaching is hard work. Being a transformational teacher takes years of conscious application of the art and science of teaching. You will see teachers who are extraordinary, and you might want to become like them. But please be aware that as you progress to becoming that kind of teacher, there will be speed bumps along the way. Be intentional about how you navigate over them. Be aware of where your sense of self is coming from. Be aware of your affirmation. Seek to create a sense of balance in your life. Take care of yourself, take care of your family, and take care of your students.

"As we wrap this up, there is a book I encourage you to read at some point in the near future. A buddy of mine gave me a copy when I was struggling to find that balance. It's by a guy named Nigel Marsh and the title is *Overworked and Underlaid: A Seriously Funny Guide to Life*. It is his very humorous take on having balance in your life. You will find yourself laughing out loud as you read it. Through humor and stories of his own life, Nigel challenges us that we have to take control of our lives rather than depending on our bosses or workplaces to help us with balance.

"Most organizations are designed to get the most out of us they can, and it is up to us to create balance. He also encourages us to have a balanced perspective on balance. His message is you can't wait until you retire to have a life outside your work. It will be too late then. He also says you don't have to take drastic action such as quitting your job to have balance. It's not about the quantity of time you spend with your loved ones or taking care of yourself, it is the quality of that time. Small things matter, according to Marsh. I'll let you borrow my copy and you can read it when you have time. We can discuss it more after that if you want."

"Thanks, Nathaniel. Of all of the topics we've discussed this year, this one really has me thinking. I certainly saw some of my own best teachers sacrificing themselves for their students, and I see myself doing that on some days as well. I feel like I'm making a difference when I stay a little later than usual to help one of them. It's the affirmation you are talking about. It's a good feeling. I'm thankful that right now I'm not in a relationship yet. When that time comes in my life, the lesson you taught me today will come in handy. It's one I'll not forget and try to learn from."

We continue to fish for another hour or so, making small talk and enjoying the challenges of catching and releasing some amazing fish. After we are both spent, we pack up and head back to the marina. I thank Nathaniel for another amazing fishing trip and lessons about being a great teacher while trying to maintain some semblance of balance.

The ethic of care . . . being caring . . . being intentional in being caring . . . for all students . . . not just those who want to learn. But remember that I can't want more for my students than they want for themselves and expect them to respond and learn just because I care. Nope . . . they've got to care to learn, but it is my responsibility to plant the seed of belief in them that they can and that they are lovable. Yes, plant a seed of belief.

OK, what else? Oh, yes, what did he call it? Some shape? Oh, right . . . the triangle of tension. Representing all those things that we need to care about as teachers (our students, our families, ourselves). Funny . . . until he explained this I had no idea. But of course we have to care for all of them. Funny how I never really gave much conscious thought about taking care of myself so that I could take care of my students. I'll have to think more about this.

And the issue with affirmation. I need to be careful here. Of course it feels good to be affirmed, like when a student tells me that today was fun and they learned something, or Nathaniel gives me the thumbs-up, or when Principal Rodriguez tells me something encouraging. I can see how that might be awfully tempting to want to put all my energy into my teaching so that those things will continue. Right now in my life, that wouldn't be such a bad thing, unless I was also compromising my health or friendships. I guess I do need to be mindful of this even now with my friends and family. I'm so glad I'm not in a significant relationship. I don't think it would be fair to the other person. I barely have enough energy for what I have going now. I love having a few new friends along with the ones from my past. It's just enough, and I'm happy with where my social life is at this time.

However, I do know that I need to be very mindful of this in the future. I hope to be married one day, and I hope to be a mom at some point, but will I be able to balance this all and still be an effective teacher? I guess I can't really know the answer until I am married and I do become a mom, but for now, I'm thankful that Nathaniel explained this to me.

And I'm humbled that he would let me inside his world enough to share something as personal as when he and Suzy struggled in their marriage. That's when his advice really hit home with me. I wonder if that's what happened to Mom and Dad when they separated for a while. It makes sense. I think I'll ask them one day.

Anyway . . . what else? Oh, yeah! I'm tired again, but love it.

EXIT SLIP NUMBER FOUR

1. *I do love the fly fishing analogy for great teaching. I will definitely continue to work towards being that teacher.*
2. *Affirmation is intoxicating. I know I need to be careful about depending on it too much.*
3. *While great teachers answer the call to become a teacher and it often becomes who you are rather than what you do, it is important to try to maintain balance.*

Nathaniel

I feel like this was a very good day with Meghan. I know I have a tendency to talk too much. But I love her enthusiasm, and there's so much I want to tell her so she can avoid many of the pitfalls I navigated along the way. I'm excited to tell Suzy about our morning as I open the back door.

She is sitting at the kitchen table with a glass of water. The newspaper is folded on the table as if it hasn't been touched. I walk over, give her a kiss on the forehead and excitedly say, "Wow, what an amazing morning. Fishing was good and we hit on some powerful stuff in terms of what it means to be a great teacher. We talked about the importance of caring and ways to show the kids you care . . . I didn't even say hello. How are you? Good morning!"

Suzy grabs my hand and motions for me to sit in the chair next to her and says, "I've been thinking about the fly fishing analogy you used last time. I would have loved to hear you mentor her these last few months. Sounds like you were on your 'A game' again this morning.

I think it's easy to talk about being a great teacher when you are one. I know I've said it before, but I am so proud of you. You are a great teacher, a loving father, and an amazing husband. I've seen you grow so much in all three of those roles. I know it hasn't always been easy, but you've managed to do all of those roles very well. I love you so much and I love the life we have together."

Somewhat taken aback, I say "Thanks. You don't have to say all of that. I know you are proud of me. Sweetie, why are you crying? What is it? Did I do something wrong? Are the kids okay?"

Suzy grabs both of my hands, smiles and says, "We need to talk. I have something I need to tell you."

"Okay," I reply nervously. "You're scaring me a little here. What's going on?"

Suzy looks at me like I've only seen her do on a few occasions, and the look always means bad news. She says, "Well, I went to see Dr. Putman yesterday. It was a follow-up to my annual physical I had last month. Nathaniel, I have cancer. Cervical cancer."

My heart immediately sinks and I feel like someone hit me with a hammer at the same time. I look away, and my first thought is she's going to die and I don't want to live without her. I begin to cry and turn my head back toward her and plead, "I don't understand. I didn't even know you were going to the doctor. How'd you find out? How bad is it? What are we going to do?"

With tears streaming down her face, Suzy squeezes my hands

even harder. "I know. I probably should have told you before, but I didn't want to worry you, and I wanted to know for sure before I said anything. It's stage 4, and I need to have a hysterectomy and go through chemo and radiation. I'm sorry I didn't tell you. Don't be upset with me."

I want to scream right now. I want to just yell as loud as I can. I can't believe what I'm hearing. This isn't supposed to happen to us. It's not supposed to happen to her. I pull her up and begin to hug her. Holding on tightly, I say, "I'm not upset. I understand why you wanted to do that part by yourself. I probably would've done it too. What do you need from me? I want to help you."

"Just hug me right now," Suzy says. "I need you to be strong for me. I'm going to beat this thing and I need you to help me."

Pulling back from her slightly and gently taking her face in my hands, I say "Of course I will. I'll be here for you in any way I can. I love you, Suzy, and we will beat this thing together. We will."

Suzy smiles slightly and looks down. "We need to call the kids. I want us to do that together. Let's call later today. I want to lie down for a while."

"Okay, can I come with you?"

"Sure," Suzy replies.

Holding hands, we walk to the bedroom. I tuck her in and go around to the other side of the bed and begin to take off my shoes. While sitting, I turn and look at her as she starts to drift off to sleep. Why is this happening? She is the love of my life and I can't imagine losing her. I remember when Janice was diagnosed with stage 4 cervical cancer. She went through hell. Tom went through hell right along with her. I remember how quickly she went from being a vibrant, engaged, caring teacher and colleague to someone who got sick very quickly. I know everyone is different, and who knows how Suzy will respond to the surgery and treatment.

Please God, let her live. I don't want to live this life without her. How am I going to do this? I know I'm supposed to be strong for her, and I'm going to do everything I can to be that for her. I just don't know if I can do it. No, I have to do it. I am going to be strong for her. Should I continue to teach? I don't think so. I need to be home with her. I want to be home with her. She probably won't want me to be there, but I want to do everything I can to help her and spend every moment I can with her. I'm going to talk to Henry on Monday and let him know I'm retiring immediately. I know he will understand. He can find someone to cover my classes for the rest of the year. I'll have to let Meghan know at some point. I'm not ready for that. I need to ask Suzy if she's okay with me telling Meghan. I don't understand. She doesn't deserve this.

CHAPTER 10

Leveling Up

Nathaniel

Meghan is already here when I arrive. This is the first time I am going fishing with her that I really don't know if I want to be here. I really enjoy it, and I'm getting as much out of it as she might be. I just feel like every minute away from Suzy is time that I'll never get back with her. It's always like that, but it just seems so much more urgent and pronounced now. I'm glad Suzy insisted that I go. I think she needs a break from my doting and constant questioning regarding how she feels.

I know she doesn't want me to say anything about her situation yet. She is such a private and proud person. I'm not going to say anything to Meghan about it. I definitely want to honor Suzy's wishes when it comes to that. I also haven't made a final decision about retiring, and I think it would be best to explain all of it together.

Meghan is leaning against her trunk and I notice a white paper bag and a couple of cups that are most likely coffee. Did she bring breakfast? I get out of the truck; walk over to her car, and say, "Hey Meghan. Good morning. How was it waking up to that clock this morning?"

Meghan smiles and replies, "Not bad at all. I actually got up earlier than usual. I stopped by Maria's and got us some *huevos rancheros* and some coffee. They probably aren't quite as good as when they come fresh off the griddle. But she wrapped them in foil and assured me they would be nice and warm. You okay if we eat before we head out?"

Opening the bag and taking in the aroma, I say, "You don't have to twist my arm too hard. Thanks for doing that. I truly believe I could eat that meal a few times a week and never tire of it. Let's eat."

We both unwrap our breakfast and take the lids off of our coffees and begin to eat. That first bite is amazing. We lean on the car and use the trunk as our makeshift table. We both take a couple of bites without saying anything, looking at our surroundings and enjoying the quietness of the moment.

The sun is starting to peek above the horizon as I think about Suzy and wish she could see the sunrise with us. She would definitely appreciate it. I am reminded of how torn I feel as I think I should be back at home with her, but I'm also committed to these outings with Meghan. Well, I'm here. I love to fish and I know Suzy wants me to be here as well.

Taking a sip of coffee, I ask Meghan, "So what sort of questions do you have this morning?

As if she's been waiting on me to ask, Meghan jumps right in. "I think I'm having some sort of enlightenment and I need your feedback. I've been thinking a great deal lately about the academic progress of my students. I feel like I'm starting to see these grouping patterns according to achievement, ability, motivation, etc. I want to help them, and me too I guess, when it comes to improving my ability to plan, instruct, motivate and remediate because I believe that's what good teachers try to do all the time.

"What I'm seeing in my classes is that I always seem to have a smaller percentage, say 15–20% that seems to 'do school well.' I would also say that there is roughly the same percentage, maybe a bit smaller that seems to struggle significantly with just about everything I give them. I don't think they are dumb, but I do think that there are a number of variables that contribute to their consistent struggles. Then, I'm most intrigued by this large middle group; it might be 60% or more of my kids that just seem to show up and take care of their business without going too high or too low. It's kind of like they are hiding in plain sight.

"The high-functioning kids certainly want my attention as a teacher and the low functioning kids certainly need it, but it is that large portion of students in the middle that intrigue me. It seems to me that with just a little more effort from me and from them I would think our overall achievement scores would go up significantly because of the size of the group."

Finishing a bite of her *huevos rancheros*, Meghan says, "So, here is my added enlightenment. You asked me to observe my profession and I'm wondering if my grouping theory regarding students applies to teachers as well. Am I crazy or not?"

"That, Ms. Donahue, is an insightful and thought-provoking observation," I say to her. "You are certainly not crazy, either. I'm impressed that you are starting to see, as opposed to just look. Instead of rushing to judgment like many people seem to do immediately, you appear to be assessing the situation. Wise educators learn to do that on a consistent basis. What you have identified in your 'noticings and wonderings' is the concept of variance and the significant middle in our educational system. You were certainly correct in identifying it from a grade/achievement perspective in students, but I feel a more significant factor in educational achievement is the variance which can occur with teachers.

"As you know, what you describe with your students is the classic bell-shaped curve theory. Your observations certainly fit the theory, but the vast majority of people never think about that grading theory as it applies to the adults in the educational system. This is especially true for teachers because they have the greatest potential for positive or negative impact on students based on contact time. An outstanding school is able to identify students in the significant middle and below and make concerted efforts to move them up in an effort to tip the curve towards higher achievement. In high performing schools I believe the same philosophy is applied by leaders to maximize teacher investment, attitude and effort as well.

"I'm going to tell you a secret. Motivation theory is far more important for teachers than it is for the students because a motivated teacher has a tremendous multiplier effect on large numbers of kids. A motivated student is wonderful but does not normally offer the same potential for positive growth in others. You were very observant to recognize this and bring it up. Well done!"

"I want to hear more about this," Meghan says. "I feel like I've identified it, but now I need you to define it for me so I can understand it."

Taking a final drink of coffee, I say, "Let's continue this while we're fishing. Thanks for breakfast. It was really good."

"Sure, my pleasure."

We clean up our trash and begin the process of getting on the water. Meghan has gotten the hang of it all, and we both know what we need to do.

Once we arrive at our fishing spot, we both get out of the boat and begin casting. I pick up where we left off in our conversation on teacher variance. "I think the best way to describe this is like drifting or floating that fishermen do at times in their boats. I say drifting or floating because I believe it best describes what a large percentage of teachers can potentially experience at different times over the course of a teaching career. All teachers should be aware of this phenomenon. Consistently productive teachers stay mindful of the symptoms. They also learn to navigate this season of their careers in order to avoid the potential pitfalls associated with drifting. Unfortunately, though, I would say there are times when it can be like catching a cold . . . unavoidable, no matter how many precautions one has taken."

Sensing a bite on her line, Meghan pulls back hard to set the hook. But this one gets away. Starting her cast again, she says, "Give me specifics. What are the symptoms? What should I be mindful of?"

"This can be a bit tricky at times," I reply, "because it requires an ability to honestly self-reflect and the willingness to have colleagues and friends in your professional life who are truth-tellers, and by that I mean people who will be honest with you even if they know you won't want to hear it. That can be a very difficult process for teachers. Heck, adults in general have a hard time putting that into practice. Most of us don't care to hear about our weaknesses and shortcomings, but if your goal is to be great and stay great, then seeing ourselves honestly is of vital importance."

Suddenly, I feel a huge strike and set the hook. Oh boy, this is going to be a big one. I let him run and then reel him in a little. I am moving all over the place trying to work him and tire him out. Ten minutes later I see this beautiful red drum. I'm thinking he must weigh 20 pounds or more. Meghan gets the net ready and we both work to get him into it. The fish is spent and so am I. I take the fly from his mouth while Meghan holds him in the net. I then pick him up, and Meghan takes a couple of pictures.

I smile as I get down on one knee and gently lower him back into the water. He pauses for a brief moment and then moves his tail and swims away. What an incredible feeling. That was fun. Meghan and I re-enact various aspects of the last ten minutes and share a few laughs.

We then both begin to cast again and I say, "So, you want specifics. First, let me tell you that I do not think this season is necessarily about bad teachers or poor instruction at all. I feel it is best defined in terms like investment, attitude, and effort. There is a coaching/performance model which I think makes great sense from a theory standpoint. I was introduced to this model by a former principal who used it with our committee in the hiring process. She said it would hopefully provide focus as to the type of individual we wished to hire. There were four descriptors: High Will, Low Will, High Skill, and Low Skill.

"From a pairing standpoint there were only four potential options. She always told us that the most important priority in her mind was to first identify individuals with High Will. She said Low Will individuals are not well-suited to be teachers and are too difficult to change. Regarding High or Low Skill she was more flexible. She said at times it is definitely nice to hire High Skill, but she has also seen situations where hiring Low Skill works well, as long as there is High Will to improve. That experience really opened my eyes as to how I looked at teachers, administrators and other professionals in their careers. I really think it speaks to what we are talking about here in the sense that I believe the core of this season is made up of teachers who, for one reason or another, are experiencing will problems. And this negatively impacts characteristics like skill, attitude, effort, and investment."

"That model makes a lot of sense," Meghan says.

"Let me give you a fishing connection," I say. "Throughout my time as a fly fisherman I have always tried to be a student of the craft. Early on I was certainly motivated and had a high will to improve. I would read books and articles, watch videos, go to clinics, and basically pick the brains of anyone I thought could help me advance my knowledge and skill. Over the years I have discovered that my best learning ultimately came from being around other fly fishermen in an effort to watch, listen, and learn. Smart teachers do the same. Not long after I arrived down here I came across some old boys who let me into their fishing world and the south Texas culture. We would gather at different places, but their favorite watering hole was the local VFW."

Looking puzzled, Meghan asks, "What is VFW? I've never heard of it."

Laughing, I reply, "VFW stands for Veterans of Foreign Wars, and is an organization that provides support for military veterans who served in foreign wars. There are posts around the country where they can seek needed help as well as hang out with people who have had similar experiences. All of the guys I hung out with proudly served their country, and I think they tolerated me because I was respectful, listened twice as much as I talked, and always bought a couple of rounds of PBRs. Those beers were kind of like my membership dues."

I pause briefly and ask, "You do know what a PBR is, don't you?"

Chuckling, Meghan replies, "Oh yeah, I know what that is. I had my fair share of that beer when I was in college."

"I thought you might," I counter.

"One day fishing class was in session at the VFW, and the topic was what makes a great fly fisherman. All of them threw their two cents in on the topic. Then one of the patriarchs, Sonny, shared an analogy that has always stuck with me. I also think it applies perfectly to what we are discussing. He said, 'Boys, being great at anything in life is a conscious decision. Someone may have some natural abilities and gifts, but it takes more than that to be great. Hell, the best way to describe it is like a fine southern breakfast of ham and eggs. Now that chicken is certainly participating, but that pig . . . there is no doubt that the pig is committed! Some people can be good at things in life by simply participating, but the great ones are truly committed.'"

Meghan stops casting and smiles. "I've definitely heard the chicken and pig analogy in terms of commitment. My grandpa sounds a lot like your buddy Sonny. He always had great stories and analogies to get his point across about lesson he wanted us to learn."

"In the simplest sense," I reply, "that is the best description I can give you of teachers in this season. There are times when a teacher could best be described as participating as opposed to being fully committed. It doesn't mean they are bad at what they do at all. I have known colleagues over the years who I would consider to be solid, strong, and even master teachers who have fallen into this season for one reason or another. The symptoms can manifest themselves in different ways. I also think this season makes the assumption that the teacher has previously achieved a solid level of professional competency. They have accumulated evidence like tenure, leadership roles, recognition, as well as peer and student respect. This demonstrates they possess the ability to be a successful teacher. Some folks just don't belong in the profession, and the concept is that those individuals would get weeded out before receiving tenure, but that's certainly not always the case either.

"Another indicator of this stage is a teacher who seems to just be going through the motions. Kids can smell this out in a heartbeat. There are positives and negatives to being in one school for a long time. At Delmar we used to have a history teacher named Peter Southwell. His class was very popular with the students. Mr. Southwell has been retired now for a few years.

"Early in my career I heard some of my students in class talking about an upcoming test in his class. They were laughing and joking about the test as opposed to showing any concern at all. I heard one of them say, 'Thank God for repeat or we would be screwed.' After class I was talking to one of the boys on the side and I said how nice it was that Mr. Southwell let students do retakes on tests. That must be one of the reasons so many kids wanted him for a teacher. Jimmy then told me that he never did that. I then asked about the repeat line I heard the boys talking about earlier. Jimmy looked at me, smiled, and said, 'Mr. Speer, we call him "RePete" as an inside joke because he has been giving the same tests for at least fifteen years.'"

"'All of our brothers and sisters had him for class. Legend has it that over a decade ago one of the kids brought his test review home to study. His sister saw it and gave him all the answers. Then word got out with the kids and everybody wanted him for class. He's a nice guy and most of the kids really like him, but the truth is they love the easy grade. Hey Shake, We're cool, right? You're not going to snitch, are you?' I thought for a minute and looked at Jimmy and said, 'We're cool. Thanks for being honest with me.' "

Meghan looks at me and asks, "Did you say anything to Mr. Southwell? I think I would want to know if students in my classes viewed me this way."

"No," I reply, "I didn't say anything because I gave Jimmy my word. Maybe I should have, but I didn't want to jeopardize the trust this student had in me. He trusted me enough to tell me what was happening. I didn't want to change that."

Continuing with my discussion of teachers who seem to be going through the motions, I say, "I remember in the first couple years of teaching having a conversation with a teaching mentor, Mr. Paxton. Looking back, he was attempting to educate me on this very topic. I was asking him about some teachers in my department because I was new and wanted to get to know my new colleagues.

"I remember saying to him about one of them, 'How many years has he been teaching?' He looked at me and without any expression said, 'Well Nathaniel, technically he has accrued thirty years on the seniority/salary schedule, but really I would say fifteen years of actually teaching.' I quickly replied, 'What do you mean by that?' He looked at me without missing a beat and said, 'He taught his butt off for the first fifteen years of his career, but for the last fifteen he has just pushed the replay button.' These are two great examples of what can happen to good teachers. Try your best to avoid being a teacher who just 'RePetes' or replays in your career.

"I think we should get in the boat and see if we can find another spot," I say. "Seems we have spooked most of the ones that might have been around here."

"Okay, I want to be the one to push us along," Meghan replies.

Handing her the pole with a smile, "Have at it."

Meghan gets the pole and climbs on the platform and starts to work. As she puts the pole in the water, she says, "I can see how teachers can fall into the trap of going through the motions. It would be easy to establish yourself and your curriculum and then just do the same thing year after year. I'd be interested to hear more about some of the signs of this season."

"It might be the teachers who seem superficially or less engaged in lesson planning and preparation," I say. "Good and effective teaching requires strong investment and a desire to 'get after it' on a daily basis for your kids. I know there have been times when I have not been my best every hour of every day, but what I have tried to do over the years is discipline myself to build and maintain both my physical and mental stamina for teaching. Then, I need to stay mindful of how I allocate those resources so I can be at my best as much as possible.

"I know teachers are easy targets for many folks because of the perception that we do less work because of summer break. However, I defy most adults to step in front of 100 to 150 teenagers every day for five different performances. Most parents I know spend a great deal of time talking about the challenges with their own children. Well if the average family has 2.5 children, multiply that by 50 or so and you have some idea of a teacher's daily responsibilities. I certainly understand that parents have direct ownership of so many factors related to their children, but over the decades more and more evidence will point to the added responsibilities and expectations which have fallen on our educational system and the teachers that teach in it.

"Another symptom which you will very likely see, are the teachers who may rest on their laurels or live off of their past accomplishments at times. It can certainly be easy to do. Consistently effective teaching requires strong doses of commitment, effort, motivation, positive attitude, resilience, grit, and likely some fear of what might happen if I underperform or don't try my best. Satchel Paige was a famous baseball pitcher in the Negro Leagues for many years. He was in his early 40s when Jackie Robinson broke the color barrier. Satchel was a rookie in the majors at 42 years old and was able to pitch for five more years. One of his most famous sayings was, 'Don't look back, because something might be gaining on you.' Sometimes I think that this is the philosophy that applies to some great teachers because they believe that if they don't give their best every day, something negative could happen to them."

"I've never heard of Satchel Paige," Meghan replies. Smiling, she says, "What a great saying. Seems very wise."

I cast another line before I continue speaking. "Another analogy I might use here is the concept of grading on a curve in school. Everyone says they want to do well, and I think for the most part that is true; but in reality, I believe many people wish for the curve and hope for the curve for a variety of reasons. It could represent the path of least resistance or the fear of failure or embarrassment based on comparisons to peers. That environment of comparison can drive people to seek the significant middle, where there is a perceived safety in numbers and certainly less perceived and real pressure. Many students and teachers can drift and still perform well, even quite well at times. But there is also fear and anxiety about reaching for consistent greatness because one knows it will likely come with potential public challenge and failure at times. That fear of not measuring up or failing usually causes many people to avoid risking a full effort. That is when some will choose to live with a B or B- in hopes that others did worse, thereby adjusting the curve upward in their favor and leaving them with a B+ or A-.

"The funny thing, though, is that the failure is usually never as bad as the fear we associate with it. In order for one to learn, it is required that one will fail. Exceptional learners master the art of failing forward and failing fast. As a society, especially in education, we have made failure a dirty word, and it has harmed our willingness to take a risk and to achieve our full potential."

"So why do you say that most teachers spend time in this season?" Meghan asks. "Why is it so prevalent?"

"In most cases the system is not designed well enough to prevent it. There is too much potential for individual teachers to drift without having some sort of warning light or alarm going off, indicating that they have fallen off course. Sometimes the reasons and causes are simple to see, but many times the indicators are much more subtle and can go undetected.

"By its nature, teaching is not a standardized activity with constant oversight and monitoring. Our educational system struggles to find good evidence pertaining to a teacher's impact on student learning. It also struggles because in most cases it chooses not to utilize monitoring tools and systems designed to ensure accountability that we see in other professions."

"Why don't we use these monitoring systems?" Meghan asks. "It seems like we should."

"To be fair, these systems can be expensive and time consuming, which is why many public school systems don't have the resources to employ them."

"Makes sense," Meghan says.

"I'm not advocating for them," I continue. "But I am saying they are certainly available if educators wanted to implement them. Let me give you an example. Last week a UPS delivery came to my house. Not surprisingly the driver was one of my former students. I happened to be in the garage when he pulled up and jumped out of his truck. Hector was always a great kid, and I wanted to see how he and his family were doing. He handed me the package and we exchanged quick pleasantries. He then politely told me he had to get going right away. I offered him a soda but he told me that every one of their delivery trucks was equipped with a GPS tracking monitor. The goal was to promote speed and efficiency while preventing downtime and employee distraction. He said supervisors regularly reviewed their daily data. He also told me it was pretty much standard practice in the delivery industry.

"Delivery expectations like that are not in place in education. That is probably good at times. However, it is probably bad as well. I don't care if you work in a school of 300 or 3,000 students and staff, teaching can be a very isolated and lonely profession if you allow it to be. Great teachers, administrators and school districts always value the power of collegial relationships. Students and staff need connection, caring and a sense of being valued. High connection and care equals higher engagement. The opposite is true as well."

Smiling, Meghan says, "Great analogy with the UPS guy. The

relationship piece also reminds me of the spaghetti and waffle discussion."

Thinking for a second, I nod in agreement.

Continuing, Meghan says, "I hear what you're saying. We could probably learn a thing or two from the corporate world when it comes to accountability and performance. Just in the short time I've been teaching, I'm not sure how many teachers would be in favor of more tracking of their performance. I understand it's difficult to measure and it can't be based solely on student performance. But it seems there should be something in place to maximize accountability."

We are getting several hits on the flies we are using, but not catching anything. It seems as though they are toying with us today.

I pause to get a couple of water bottles, throw one to Meghan, and take a sip from my own. "I said earlier that teaching is about understanding social science and psychology. I believe that is true. But it doesn't happen without the teacher being present, invested and engaged. You are probably thinking of that in the physical sense. That is certainly true and required, but I am going to take it up several notches and tell you that the true secret to being a successful teacher is when you can do that from an emotional perspective as well.

"Educational utopia is achieved when those two states have a symbiotic relationship and function in harmony. It's like when you are fly fishing and everything seems to align perfectly for whatever reason. The water conditions, temperature, fishing gear, your mental state, timing the hatch, everything. For purists, it becomes the challenge of not only seeking perfection, but more importantly, elongating the experience as much as possible with the ultimate goal of solving the riddle of how to get to that place on a regular basis.

"I would hope that every teacher would strive for that utopian state every hour of the day for every day of the school year. Impossible to accomplish? Most likely, and that is what can cause teachers to drift many times. The journey to being good and great on a consistent basis can be challenging for many folks. I get angry about it sometimes when I see colleagues or students drifting. But a couple of years back, I learned something very valuable from one of my students which I feel applies to this stage.

"His name was Benny. He was a sophomore in one of my English classes. I felt that I just couldn't break through with him to get him excited about reading literature and English. I was casting about every fly I had, and Benny was just not taking the bait. I finally realized, like you did when you made a comment about your student's recently dyed hair, I may need to put myself in his world in order to find a way in with him. I started to observe Benny more around school, and I talked to some of my students who knew him pretty well. What I learned was that Benny was a gamer. I do stay current enough to know that meant that he enjoyed playing video games. Bingo. I found the right bait. Little did I know that my technique would be way off, and Benny would teach me a thing or two about fishing.

"The next week in class I was doing some individual conferences with my English students about their reading lives. Benny was on my schedule. Expertly, I navigated our conversation to hobbies, and I asked him if he liked to play video games, knowing what the answer would be. All of a sudden Benny's eyes lit up and he responded, 'I love to play video games, Mr. Speer, primarily Call of Duty. I'm pretty good.'"

"Being the strategist that I am, I already knew that from a prior conversation with one of his friends. I also asked enough questions and did enough research to realize that Benny was never going to win that game. My goal would be to get him to realize that and then invest some of that time into literature and reading, which I felt would improve his life immensely.

"I turned to him and said, 'That's wonderful, Benny, but you know that you are never going to win Call of Duty, don't you? I'm not trying to burst your bubble, but don't you think some of the time you devote to playing could be better served on reading and improving your grade in English? You are always going to end up dying when you play that game.'"

"Without hesitation Benny looked up at me and smiled. I will never forget what he shared with me. 'It's not about winning, Mr. Speer. It's about dying later! I'm just trying my best to level up every day.'

"His gamer academic vocabulary was losing me now. 'I apologize, Benny,' I said. 'I don't play video games and my kids have been out of the house a while now. What does level up mean?'

"Laughing, Benny replied, 'It basically means improving enough to achieve the next level of the game. Over the last few months I have improved four levels. I don't play to win, Mr. Speer. I play to die later, which means I'm getting better and figuring out a system. I really like you, but I have a hard time getting excited about reading *Romeo and Juliet* or *The Odyssey*. I get Call of Duty.'"

"Wow. Talk about feeling foolish and excited at the same time. Simultaneously, Benny was not only able to make me aware of how inane my strategy was to get him to give up some gaming for more reading; he was also able to enlighten me about a gamer's guide to grit, resilience and perseverance.

"From that point on I started seeking out books and articles on gaming and game theory for Benny to read. I also was able to benefit as a teacher from his explanation of leveling up. When I thought about it, that is exactly what Odysseus was trying to do as he was navigating multiple challenges created for him and his men. His goal for them was to die later and keep moving forward."

Meghan takes a long drink of water and says, "That's an interesting connection you are making with Odysseus. I wonder if Benny would get that connection if you used it with him."

"I hadn't thought of that. I need to remember to use that with him."

Finishing my water, I say, "My experience with Benny helped me better understand this season. You have started to notice differences in teachers when it comes to things like attitude, effort, and skills. For whatever reason, some teachers stop their pursuit of excellence and drift. In an ideal world we wish that they would keep trying to level up and improve, but for some reason their progress is thwarted. I believe most teachers see this as that timeout or pit stop in order to get resources, then get back at it, but I would be lying if I said that everybody is prompt and motivated to get back on the road. Just like with our students, learning happens for individuals on different days and in different ways."

"Tell me about when . . . Oh, I've got one."

Meghan has a fish on the line and is working it. I get the net from the boat and watch as she reels it in. She has definitely got the hang of this type of fly fishing. She brings in a nice trout. I ask if she wants a picture and she says, "Nah, I'm good."

She brings the fish into the palms of her hands for just a few seconds and says, "I want you to know I have been paying attention. This is just what we've talked about with the analogy of great teaching and fly fishing. I used a fly this fish was attracted to and caught it. I then brought it into my hands for a short period of time and now I'm going to release it. I really do like the analogy."

Meghan releases the fish and asks, "What was I saying before?"

"You started to say tell me about—"

"Right," Meghan quickly adds. "Tell me about when you went through it. What was it like?"

We both continue to cast our lines as I say, "It's definitely something that I feel occurs for most teachers at different times in their careers. Looking back now I can definitely see times where I chose to drift for different reasons. Early in my career I would say that I lacked discipline and purpose at times. I had plenty of energy, but I lacked a plan or an understanding for how to ration it and use it most effectively. At times my students didn't always get my best, nor did some of their papers when it came to how I graded writing assignments. The pacing of my teaching, along with the creation and development of my classroom learning environment, left much to be desired. Now, in retrospect, I can forgive myself because I realized that I was in that first season trying to survive as a new teacher. I think that is pretty normal. What becomes tough to forgive is when some teachers consciously choose to drift as a means to avoid leveling up and getting better.

"I see it happening regularly to teachers who also coach, especially high school varsity sports where the expectations for success by various stakeholders have skewed the professional responsibility perspective. You should be able to appreciate this because we live in Texas, where high school football reigns supreme in many people's eyes. I did not have a handle on that as a teacher coming from out of state when I arrived.

"Remember, I told you I desperately wanted that first job and agreed to take the job that included an assistant's position with the freshman football team. I liked football but I was certainly no Joe Paterno or, let's see . . . um, Mack Brown, but as soon as they heard that I was willing to coach football, they hired me. I thought, *No big deal*. Little did I know that high school football was a huge deal in Texas, even at the freshman level."

"Believe me, I know about Texas high school football," Meghan says. "Both of my brothers played it and it was king at my high school."

"So you do get it," I reply. "Anyway, I 'hit the ground running' as an assistant coach. I monitored summer weight room workouts and participated in the daily meetings the head coach scheduled. Our schedule got even more hectic as the school year approached. I was trying to find time to meet with my department chair in the English department, and the head coach just looked at me like I was committing a mortal sin. Now Coach Leavenworth was a good man and a fine coach, but academic teaching was not high on his radar. That guy was something. He used to always do this thing when he would meet new players, or parents, or even officials for the first time. He would extend his hand with a firm grip and say, 'My name is Leavenworth . . . Coach Leavenworth . . . Just like the prison!' He loved to shake folks up, and he was one tough son of a gun. He used to love to go a little crazy when trying to motivate players. I remember him jumping into full contact drills in his shorts and t-shirt telling kids to block him at full speed. On multiple occasions I remember Coach getting his face bloodied from head to helmet contact in those drills.

"At that point I realized it was going to be a long year for me academically. I wasn't ready to bleed for the football program, but it sure did eat up an inordinate amount of my time. It forced me to drift and place my classroom responsibilities after my football coaching. Funny thing was that no one called me on it. My principal, the department chair, my colleagues, the students and the parents all gave me a pass because they knew I was a football coach. It was embedded in the culture to the point that academic performance was not even a close second to the expectations for success placed on the football program. That spring I spoke with my principal and negotiated a 'pardon' from Leavenworth prison. It made me a far wiser and more effective teacher.

"I do want to say that some coaches are amazing teachers in addition to being great coaches. It's just very difficult to maintain a high level of commitment to both areas without running yourself into the ground or starting to drift in one area. Remember that all cultures are unique, and it just doesn't have to be something like football that causes teachers to drift at times.

"I've seen people become threatened by a new colleague or administrator and go into protection mode. I did have a former colleague who felt he was wronged when a principal shifted him out of his senior honors and advanced placement courses in favor of another instructor.

"The teacher was a veteran and felt that he had earned the right to teach the honors classes based on age. He wanted nothing to do with freshmen. The change was the right thing to do for the kids, even though it wasn't popular with some of the staff who felt as though the teacher earned the right to those honors classes. I remember the aggrieved teacher complaining that the principal told him that 'age doesn't necessarily equate to expertise.' I didn't completely get that at the time, but over the years I have grown to appreciate the wisdom in that logic.

"Well, old Mr. Whiteside proceeded to have a pity party for himself for the next couple of years. He drifted as much as possible and lived angry until he retired. He had smart kids in his classes, so it was easy to get results. For a fisherman it would be the equivalent of bragging about your results when, unbeknownst to the vast majority of people, you fish on a trout farm."

"That's funny," Meghan says with a laugh.

"The moral of this story is that in life, this kind of stuff actually happens. As the saying goes, 'Men plan and God laughs.' We aren't always in control. It's even more difficult for us as teachers because we believe we can plan and prepare ourselves for anything. A subject like English can be even more difficult because of all the time investment grading essays and research papers. Doing the job well can require massive amounts of time. It can become easy at times to drift and not fully engage. It can also be easy to spread yourself too thin with coaching, clubs, and other professional and personal responsibilities and interests which can literally grind a teacher down and force drifting for survival.

"From a professional perspective, you will need to learn to say no at times when you are asked to sponsor a club, coach a team, work events, or chaperone a dance. As we discussed last time, you need to have some balance in your life, but you also need to learn to say no at times to people or opportunities that may dominate too much of your time and cause you to lose professional balance. You need to know that the voices in your head will always be there trying to convince you that just enough is good enough. Sometimes they may win, but in the long haul you need to learn how to master them. It's not always easy and it takes practice. It took me years to understand, and it still requires self-discipline and control because the choice is always available."

Meghan nods her head again. "That message of balance clearly came through as we were discussing the challenge of pursuing greatness as a teacher and not losing yourself completely in it. Believe me, I know I have to say yes at times and actually want to say yes. I just need to remember it's okay to say no at times. We will see how that goes."

I look at my watch and ask Meghan, "What do you think? You about ready to head back? I think I'm about ready."

Meghan starts reeling in her line. "Yep, I'm ready."

We both make our way onto the boat. I sit, and am about to grab the pole to push us into deeper water, and I pause. "One last aspect of this drifting stage we are discussing is that I firmly believe many teachers choose to drift out of fear and anxiety. They are nervous that they may not measure up to their colleagues in terms of academic outcomes, or they may feel as though they may not be as liked as other teachers.

"One of my favorite books is by a highly successful college squash coach, Paul Assaiante. It's called *Run to the Roar.* The title is derived from a story he tells about how lions hunt their prey in Africa. He says that when they are hunting, the pride of lions will let one of the oldest lions go out on the savannah and lay down by himself. The lion once was a great hunter, but age has robbed him of his speed, agility, and strength. He can no longer participate in an active role. The one thing he still possesses, along with the wisdom of his years, is his great roar. Well, later in the day the zebras and hyenas begin to populate the savannah, coming ever closer to the old lion but not seeing him as a threat. Then, without provocation or warning, the venerable lion rises up and lets out his lusty roar. What do you think happens next?"

"They probably all run away because they are scared of his roar."

"Exactly," I say. "They are frightened of his roar and they flee. The problem for them, and their ultimate demise, is the rest of the pride knew they would run, and they waited on the perimeter as their prey delivered themselves up for slaughter. Assaiante used this story to make a point about why he chose to coach or teach kids. He would tell them that the vast majority of people instinctively run from what they fear in order to avoid it.

"His job was to teach them to run toward their fears and anxieties in order to better understand them. It is through that understanding that one removes the fear and overcomes. For whatever the reason, many people are not up to the task and avoid total investment and full commitment. I never want that for you. I so badly want you to never lose your desire to go and find that utopian place that reinforces to you in every imaginable way why you wanted to become a teacher. I hope that in some way that makes sense to you."

"It makes sense," Meghan replies, "I hope I will always try to level up and run to the roar."

"Well done and well said. That's the best answer given to one of my formative assessment questions in a long time. When you feel like you're struggling with being fully committed as a teacher, remember good old Sonny and go order some ham and eggs. It always helps me."

Meghan

Another great morning fishing with Nathaniel! Every time we come out here I think that he can't possibly teach me as much as the time before. I also think that the weather won't be as good or the fish won't be as plentiful or something will go wrong with the boat. But nope, always good and always powerful. Well, except for that one Saturday, but the food at breakfast more than made up for loss of time on the water.

So what did I learn today? Teachers drifting, seemingly going nowhere with no course and no purpose and simply going through the motions trying to stay under the radar. Yep, I've seen those. My question has always been why? Why does this happen? His explanation of leveling up really made sense to me. It requires going to the next level to want to prolong the game. Never thought of this before. Yes, it works in video games and in the corporate world, I guess . . . but in education . . . nope. I guess as long as a teacher has earned tenure or isn't doing too much wrong to draw attention to themselves or hasn't committed a crime, they can simply drift along. Come to think about it, there really is no incentive not to do this except for one's own work ethic. Boy, I sure do hope that I don't become complacent like this. Why would someone continue just going along being complacent, not caring to grow any more in their own craft? That can't be satisfying.

And the whole bell curve thing. Yep, I get this. I know I wanted to be graded on the curve, especially in those subjects where I struggled. At the time it seemed great to get a grade of C for work that was more worthy of a D or even an F. But when I think of teaching, I think I want to argue against grading teachers on the bell curve. To do that would mean that the vast majority of teachers would earn a grade of C for teaching. Average? Really? Since when is it acceptable for us as teachers to be satisfied with a C? We should want to be A's. At least I sure do.

And when I think of being a parent one day, would I really want my child to be taught by an "average" teacher? I think not! And from the other perspective, if, as a teacher, the majority of my students emerge from my classes with a grade of C, doesn't that make me an average teacher? A mediocre teacher at best? I don't want that for me or my students.

OK . . . this whole topic has really fired me up today. I feel more motivated than ever to really examine my motives as I teach. Am I going to be willing to level up as needed? Am I willing to disrupt the bell curve?

EXIT SLIP NUMBER FIVE

1. *This stage is more teacher-centered than student-centered.*
2. *It doesn't necessarily mean a person is a bad teacher here. It's just that they are likely less effective than they could be.*
3. *Teachers here tend to fly under the radar and are okay with the status quo. They are comfortable with being comfortable. I am going to be aware of this tendency and try to spend very little time in this space.*

Nathaniel

I feel a little guilty as I drive home. I had such a good morning fishing and talking teaching with Meghan and yet I know Suzy is home and probably not feeling very well. It was a nice escape for a few hours. I hope she's feeling okay today. Maybe she will ultimately beat this thing. I've heard of stranger things happening. I begin to feel tears well up in my eyes as I drive down the road towards the love of my life. I don't want to lose her.

I arrive home and she's asleep. I'm not going to wake her. I've really enjoyed sharing with her the lessons that Meghan and I discuss. We can talk about that later. She looks so peaceful sleeping. I don't understand why this is happening to her now. I don't know that I'll ever understand why. They say God always has a plan, but it sure doesn't make sense to me. I'm going to remain strong for her. I have to be positive with her. She is being so strong. I can't bring her down because I am sad and scared. But I also can't help thinking she is young, and our grandkids are going to miss out on the opportunity to know her if she can't beat it. She is an incredible grandmother, mother, and wife. I would miss her so much. I don't want to think about life without her right now. I think I'll just lie down beside her and hold her.

Suzy turns over and says, "Hi, you."

CHAPTER 11

The Power in Our Stories

Meghan

He hasn't been himself lately. I can tell something is different with him. It isn't a huge deal, but I feel I've gotten to know him somewhat over the last few months, and he just doesn't seem to have that same "spring in his step" or that "gleam in his eye" that I am used to seeing. I hope he is still enjoying these little fishing trips we do. Maybe it's too often or maybe I'm asking too many questions. Maybe something is going on with his family or his health. I want to ask him, but I don't want to pry or make a big deal of something that isn't.

He's here before me and he's putting the boat in the water. That's a good sign. I'm going to just see how it goes. I'm probably overly sensitive. I just enjoy these Saturday mornings. He's smiling. That's good. Relax, Meghan, it's going to be a great day. "Good morning," I say to him. "What a beautiful morning this is going to be. It's late Fall and it's still pretty warm. This is different than Dallas, and night and day from Alaska at this time of year."

"Hey there," Nathaniel replies. "No doubt, it's a beautiful morning. I love this time of year down here. I don't miss the Philly winters myself. You ready to catch some fish? I think we're going to have a great morning on the water. The conditions are as good as I've ever seen."

"I'm totally ready," I say. "Do you ever stop and think about how many people would love to do what we get to do? I know I've been thinking so much about that lately."

"I think about it all the time," Nathaniel says. "I know I'm a lucky man. I've been fishing this place for half my life and I try to never take it for granted. Like you, I've been thinking about it even more lately. We are truly blessed. I hope you will always try to be grateful for experiences like this and the people in your life that you care about. You never know what might happen or how long you will be able to be with those people or have those experiences."

"You're right," I reply. "I definitely don't want to take any of it for granted."

Smiling, Nathaniel responds, "All right Let's go. Those fish are waiting for you and me to dance those flies right out there where they can't resist. I'm looking forward to hearing the questions you have for me. Wondering what you have been noticing and wondering about lately. We can talk when we get out there."

I ask to drive the boat and Nathaniel is happy to let me. He says we are going to a totally different spot to begin with this morning. He's heard from some of his buddies that the fish have been feeding there pretty regularly lately. As we begin to head that way, I once again think about how beautiful this place is in the early morning. It's so quiet and majestic. We are the only ones on the water.

It takes a little longer to get to our spot, but I'm anxious to see how it goes. Nathaniel motions for me to cut the engine, and as we coast, I grab the pole and start to push us along. We go about 50 yards or so and Nathaniel points straight ahead. What an amazing site. You can actually see the fish feeding. Their tails are coming up out of the water. We stop 20 feet from them and quietly get out of the boat and start to cast.

It's incredible. For the next hour we catch more fish than we've caught in all of our trips combined. It seems like we catch one every time we lay the fly out there in front of them. They are jumping at everything we throw at them. We aren't talking about anything other than how much fun we are having. I can't help but think about how this scene is much like when a teacher is engaging with students and the energy level is high. Much learning is happening because of the connection. We finally take a break and sit in the boat and enjoy the stillness.

I begin, "I'm continuing to notice and wonder at school every chance I get. I've gotten to know almost all of the teachers in this school fairly well over the past few months. While almost all of them seem to be doing a good job and enjoy working here, I've noticed two teachers, Henry Burton and Heather Riley, who don't seem to enjoy their work at all. I can hear Mr. Burton raise his voice in anger with his students at times. He doesn't seem to care what he says to them or how it may affect them. Mrs. Riley just seems to be checked out. I've heard students complain about how she doesn't care about them. Even though she teaches in our department, she rarely participates in meetings, does the bare minimum, and just seems exhausted and miserable. So my question for you is, why don't they leave and do something else? More importantly, what causes someone who has decided to devote their life to teaching to cease to care about his students, about his school, and about his profession? And, most importantly, how do I not become that?"

Pouring both of us a cup of coffee from his thermos and taking a sip, Nathaniel says, "This is a tough one, Meghan. Yes, Mr. Burton yells at his students and Mrs. Riley doesn't seem to care. Unfortunately, this is their reality at this time in their lives. And quite honestly over the course of my career, I too have had my moments where it was really hard to care. I mean all of us have had those days. Those are the really hard days or times in our lives when we question why we are doing what we are doing and simply don't seem to have the energy to continue to care anymore. I'm talking about a different level of apathy and discontent than what we've discussed before. And, as always, I trust that you will understand and use these stories to learn about what it means to be a teacher.

"First of all, Mr. Burton. Henry Burton came to this school over 20 years ago and has been teaching probably 35 years now. Like most of us, when Henry arrived here, he wasn't like he is now. He was a good teacher. Maybe not spectacular, but good enough. He seemed to enjoy his work and persevered for years. I started to see the Henry Burton that you now see begin to emerge about five years ago.

"Like many of us, as we age our bodies begin to break down. What we could do at 30 becomes pretty hard to do at 50 and beyond. Anyway, Henry ran into some serious health issues. As you know, he is not the healthiest of folks. Like many of us, he has gradually put on weight and became more sedentary in his lifestyle. I was really concerned for Henry and tried to talk with him several times about taking care of himself. I even invited him to work out with me after school and gave him some nutritional advice. He seemed to want to take care of himself, but he never really made the change in his lifestyle that would allow this to happen.

"Five years ago, Henry had his first heart attack. It happened at the end of the school year. That was followed by a triple bypass. His recovery was long and arduous over that summer, but he returned to teaching in the Fall. We all thought that he would be the same old Henry when he returned, but he wasn't. He had changed. He seemed colder and more distant from us. He didn't smile as much. Honestly, I think he was afraid. He had come through a very challenging situation, and yet, while I believed that he would use it to transform his health, instead it seems to have made him mad at life. It doesn't make it okay, but it is understandable.

"Henry is mad at life, he is mad at God, he is just plain mad at everything and, unfortunately, his students get the worst of it. It doesn't make it right. It just makes it real. What you have seen and heard from Henry unfortunately can be typical for a teacher who is hurting. In Henry's case, his body hurts and has betrayed him and he's mad at the world, I think. It's been suggested that it may be time for him to retire, but he seems to be hanging on for some reason.

"Why do you think he's hanging on?" I ask. "It seems he would be much happier if he retired."

"I don't know for sure why he's still teaching. I assume he would have his full retirement from the state based on his age and years of service. I would only be speculating if I tried to explain why. We probably have Henry for a couple more years.

"Then there is Heather," Nathaniel continues. "Again, the

Heather Riley you see today is not the same as the Heather Riley of just a few years ago. Don't forget, it's easy for us to sit in judgment of others. Remember that first conversation we had back at Nell's? I encouraged you then, be careful not to judge. Merely seek to understand. So, as we notice these things and wonder about them, remember there is always a story.

"Heather has been teaching for probably eight years. She was very much like you when she got here. She was another teacher that I kind of took under my wing. I spent some time working with her and observing her teach. My work with her was different than my work with you now. With her, the focus was on perfecting lessons, class management, and assessment. With you, it's been more about helping you become a teacher who changes lives. With her, it was about the mechanics of teaching, and with you it's been about being a teacher.

"Anyway, Heather was a good young teacher. Then two years ago, she received some bad news that would change her life. Heather and her husband had been married for about seven years. They had a young son who was three when he was finally diagnosed with autism, and he is on the extreme end of the spectrum. He is five now. Heather took this news hard. She and her husband have done everything since to provide him with the necessary therapies, but it is simply exhausting and overwhelming for her. Because she was once like you to me, she had confided on several occasions that she feels guilty all the time. She wants to leave her teaching job to be able to devote more time to him but can't afford it financially. Last year, her husband was laid off and still has not landed another job. The last time we talked about it, she mentioned they were thinking of moving back to Utah to be closer to her family."

"I can't imagine," I say with a level of guilt for being so judgmental.

"All of this worry coupled with exhaustion has clearly taken a toll on her passion for teaching. So yes, Heather can no longer care about teaching. Her capacity to care at all, even for herself, is seriously diminished. Again, it doesn't make it right. It simply makes it real. Do I wish it wasn't so? Do I wish that the old

Heather would walk back into school and have the fire and passion for teaching again? Do I wish I could hear her laughter in our department meetings again when she'd crack a joke? Yes, I wish it were so. But for now, it isn't."

Looking off into the distance, I say, "Wow, both of these stories are so sad. I'm glad that never happened to you. I wouldn't be learning all of this from you if it had ever happened to you."

"Well, it has actually happened to me," Nathaniel replies. "Life sort of cut my knees right out from under me and left me face down on the floor."

Puzzled, I respond, "But you're here. You are passionate about teaching. Your kids love you. We all love you. And you just won the Texas Teacher of the Year Award. I wouldn't have thought that anything like that might have happened to you."

Nathaniel squirms a bit, stares toward the horizon and pauses for a long moment. He looks down and for the first time, he isn't really looking at me when he is talking. I can tell he's going to talk about something that is difficult for him.

He begins: "It was the hardest time in my life. I am forever thankful that it happened. I wouldn't be who I am today without experiencing what I went through. And I wouldn't be able to empathize with both Henry and Heather if I'd not been through a valley experience. You know what I mean? About the valley?"

"No, I'm not sure I do know what you mean," I reply.

"Well, over the course of your teaching career, there will be peaks and there will be valleys. There will be times when you know, in the moment of your teaching, that this is as good as it gets. Remember the Jack Nicholson film *As Good as It Gets*? It's one of my favorite because he asks at one point, 'What if this is as good as it gets?' Now, in the movie, the Jack Nicholson character had a lot of issues and struggled to deal with them. He asked that question wondering if this was all there is, if this was as good as it gets. The peaks and valleys refer to those mountaintop moments when all is right with the world and it IS as good as it gets. The valleys then are those lowest of the low moments when nothing seems to be going right. And in between the peaks and the valleys is where most of us are on most days. The peaks are the highest highs and the valleys are the lowest lows. It's when we are in our valleys that the struggle is real. So I'm going to tell you about my worst valley."

Feeling a bit awkward, I say, "I'm sorry. Please don't feel like you have to. I didn't mean to bring up something that would be painful for you.

"It's okay," Nathaniel says. "It's a story I don't share often, but I don't mind sharing it with you. Remember, your stories should be shared with others. They are not your own. They belong to the world. They need to be told so that others can learn from them. Our shared experience is what makes us human. So here's my story.

"It was 2006. I was 43 years old. It was a Sunday, and my phone rang. Before I answered it, I knew. I knew that something bad had happened. I can't tell you how I knew it, but I knew it as well as I knew my own name. I answered the phone and it was my dad calling to tell me that my mother had been in a car accident and they were taking her to the hospital. I turned to Suzy and told her. Immediately, she said, 'You need to go. You need to go home.' She got online and booked a ticket right away. The flight was leaving in a few hours. I called my dad back and said 'I'm coming.' When I got to the hospital, I gathered with my sister and two brothers around the bedside of my mother. She was in a coma and not expected to live. She was on life support.

"For five agonizing days, we sat and prayed and held her hand saying our goodbyes. Then, when it was conclusive that there was no longer any sign of life, we made the decision to turn off the machines that were keeping her alive. She would have wanted it that way. Suzy and the kids flew in the night before we did it. Although terribly difficult, I'm so thankful that all of her children and grandchildren were able to surround her and be there for my dad as we said our last goodbyes. I like to think that she heard us and knew we were there.

"When it was over, of course, there was the funeral. Seeing more extended family members and all of our old friends from the past stirred up lots of emotions. I thought that ten-day period of time was the hardest of my life. Little did I know that the next year would be even harder. You see, when my mom died, something died in me. My mom had been my rock and my inspiration. She always knew what to say to me. In many ways, she was the glue that held our family together through thick and thin.

"I remember thinking, *How will we make it? Will my dad ever recover from this? Why did this have to happen now?* I never got a chance to say goodbye to my mom, and while I know that death is always hard, there was no closure for me. And I missed her so much. Although I didn't see her often then, she and dad would visit once or twice a year, and we always managed to make it back home every other Christmas. Anyway, my heart hurt in my grief.

"I returned to school and everyone was sympathetic and very helpful, but I was numb. It felt like I was going through the motions of life. I was trying to be myself, but I didn't seem capable of it. I simply shut down.

"As the days of my grief turned into weeks and then into months, I wondered if I would ever laugh again. I did my best to put on the happy face at school, but I could not invest the energy or the enthusiasm that I used to have for my work. I had nothing left to give to anyone. I was so sad, and I missed my mom. Of course, I also couldn't really show this side of myself to most people. Everyone expected me to be okay. Suzy was the exception. She knew. Because we had healed our marriage and worked very intentionally to be there for each other always, she became my rock. Honestly, I didn't want to teach.

"What I know now that I didn't know then was that I had sunk into a depression driven from my grief. I was going through the motions of life and had difficulty caring about anything. But Suzy insisted. She encouraged and cajoled. She listened and was there for me. She held me together like my mom had held my family together. It couldn't have been easy for her. You know, grief affects people differently. I think it is the toughest and strongest of all human emotions because it's so painful. We grieve because we loved. We don't grieve people who we don't love. We grieve those that we do. And the depth of our grief is proportional to the depth of our love for that person. I deeply loved my mom, and honestly, I could not imagine my life without her in it. So I grieved . . . deeply."

All I can think to say is, "I'm so sorry."

Nathaniel continues, "Suzy stood by my side. She loved me. She let me cry, and boy did I cry. This ol' tough guy cried every day for several weeks. But slowly over the course of about six months, the pain faded. It's not the same for everyone, but the worst of it for me lasted several months. During that time, if you would have seen me then, you would have thought that I was one of those teachers who was 'retired on my feet.' You would have thought I was one of those burned out teachers, because I really didn't care about anything.

"However, the good news is that it is possible to recover from being in this stage or season of teaching. I know because I've experienced it personally. It wasn't overnight, but it did happen. I not only came back to being my old self, but I gradually became a better person and certainly a better teacher because of it. You see, I'd never known grief like I experienced it then. I'd never experienced depression like I experienced it then. Because of coming to know what grief and depression feel like, I had a whole new understanding of what my students experienced if one of their parents died or if they were dealing with depression.

"Meghan, I believe that when we are meant to know something, it becomes made known to us. I was meant to know about grief and about depression. It was made known to me through the tragic death of my mom. But by knowing it, I can now empathize and care for others, whether it is students, colleagues, friends, or family members, when they go through a similar valley experience.

"Thankfully, I made it through. Suzy gets most of the credit for this. But my point is that sometimes being burned out or 'retired on your feet' is a temporary condition. Sometimes, the inability to care is simply a point in time in the story of our life. And with help, hope and time—and maybe a bit of luck—we come out of it. And we're not done yet. I'm still not done yet. This dark valley in my life has helped me to see life as a gift, and we must cherish each day and each moment that we are granted."

At this point, tears are overflowing and running down my cheeks. I'm looking for something to wipe my eyes and I can't find anything. I use the back of my hand and wipe several times. I take a deep breath. "Thank you. I don't know what to say. All I can say is that I am so very thankful that our paths have crossed and that you have come into my life. As you know, I am a woman of faith. I believe everything that happens to us, happens for a reason. Although I haven't lost a parent, I know that day will come. But I do know how it feels to be hurting and to have something painful happen to you to the point of questioning whether you want to go on.

"I lost my cousin, Andy, to suicide. I was 17. He was 20 and the best of all of my cousins. No one saw it coming. And then he was gone. Although not the same as losing a mother, it was my first brush with death and grief. I was a senior in high school and we had been close. Anyway, it was hard. But because of that loss, I have a particular soft spot in my heart for students that may be hurting. I think I am very sensitive to their hurt. I notice them in my classes. I see the look in their eyes. I am drawn to them and care for them since they clearly are in need of being cared for. Thanks for sharing your story with me. Thank you for letting me know that behind every teacher I see lies a story. I will seek to know the story rather than judge what I see unfairly."

"Yes," Nathaniel adds. "That's part of the reason that I say I'm thankful that I experienced such grief. Obviously, I would love for my mom to still be here with us. However, like you, that experience helped me to see kids in a different light when they might be struggling. I would say I am much more aware and empathetic.

"I also want to make it clear that some teachers should definitely not be teaching. I told you about Jim Tingle, the department chair. I have also worked with other colleagues who took advantage of a system that often protects poor teachers. There are teachers who agree to have student teachers, not so they can mentor them and gradually bring them along, but so they can give them the keys to the classroom and have them teach the classes. They see it as an opportunity to take a break from teaching. Obviously, the students in the classroom and the student teacher suffer as their development is stifled. This teacher is clearly neglecting responsibility and only cares about himself.

"There are other teachers who get to a point in their careers where they are no longer willing to stay up to date with teaching methods or technology. Students and the technology they use today are very different than they were ten to fifteen years ago, and teachers must continually evolve with them. Unfortunately, you can walk by some classrooms and the teacher is always the only one talking. She is lecturing in the traditional style that she has been doing since the beginning of her career. Students are either feverishly taking notes or disengaged. Either way, communication is one way, and we both know that isn't the most effective form of teaching for meaningful learning to take place. Any time you overuse one form of instruction, you are probably doing so because it is easier on you. I had two teachers in high school that were very ineffective. They came across as lazy. One showed videos almost every day and the other used worksheets as the instructional method of choice. Teachers at this point in their careers are clearly 'retired on their feet,' and once again the students are the ones who lose."

I nod my head in agreement. "I had a couple of those types of teachers in school as well and have always said I never want to get to that point. I know it isn't easy to 'bring your A game' every day. But I hope I am self-aware enough to know if I ever get to that point and am able to find a way to get out of it."

Nathaniel takes a deep breath and smiles at me. "This has been great conversation this morning. I know we only fished for a short time, but we sure made the most of it. I say we head back."

We get everything ready and set off for the marina. We are both in complete silence as we head back. After we load the boat on the trailer and get ready to leave, Nathaniel says, "I think being self-aware is the key. While difficult, it is imperative that we are continually aware of where we are in our career as a teacher and mentor. I don't think anyone sets out to be a teacher who takes advantage of the system or who undermines student achievement and motivation. However, we all have to be willing to admit it could happen to us. Life happens, and those challenges can affect who we are as teachers. We all become exhausted at times and perhaps question why we are teaching. Students can be frustrating, parents can be unreasonable, and we are constantly bombarded with new standards. We are human, and these factors affect us. The key is to always come back to why we chose this profession. It is to make a significant difference in the lives of each of our students in a positive and meaningful way."

I think I got sunburned on my face today. The sun reflecting off the water was more intense than usual, and I should have put more sunscreen on. That seems strange to me that I should have put sunscreen on my face this late in the year. My skin feels tender, and so does my heart. Today, even though we had an incredible hour of action, fishing was definitely an after-thought. We fished, but today I was convicted of my own lack of understanding of other teachers. Nathaniel made me realize that I had been judging two other teachers without truly knowing their circumstances or their story. It's so easy to forget that we are all human. We all struggle. At times, we fail. And in those struggles and failures, there is real pain that might cause us to cease to care about anything.

I need to be much more aware of this and make sure to catch myself if I find myself judging another teacher, assuming that they are burned out and just don't care. Nathaniel showed me that there can be very real and valid reasons why this happens, and I need to be less quick to judge and more quick to empathize and try to understand. I never thought about burnout that way. I mean, there are lots of people I know that have burned out on something at some time or another. I really appreciated learning about the difference between temporary burnout and terminal burnout. That helped.

I am struck again by Nathaniel's willingness to let me into his life. He feels more like a father to me than a mentor. He's opened up about his struggles with depression and losing his mom and how Suzy held him together. I would never have thought that he would ever have had to deal with that. She is amazing. Nathaniel says that she doesn't like being on the water much or fishing at all. How gracious of her to encourage him to take me fishing. I love how he refers to her as his rock.

My thoughts have turned to Andy. He truly was the best of all of us. Nathaniel's story of loss triggered my own. I couldn't help crying today. And Nathaniel understood. We shared a moment. I felt vulnerable, and yet Nathaniel used his story of grief and my own as an example to teach me about having empathy for others. My soul has been stirred today, and my heart touched. My skin is tender and my heart is full. How lucky am I to get to do this?

EXIT SLIP NUMBER SIX

1. *Like a few of the other situations Nathaniel and I have discussed, teachers in this season tend to focus on themselves rather than what is best for their students.*
2. *Teachers no longer care when they get to this point in their careers.*
3. *A teacher's time here can be temporary, where you can't care because something traumatic happens to you, or more terminal because you choose not to care.*

Nathaniel

I feel like I was talking about myself this morning when I was describing why Henry and Heather are struggling. I'm finding it more and more difficult to spend the emotional energy needed to be the teacher that I'm telling Meghan we should all strive to be. I don't think I'm being hypocritical, but I also know I have to try to compartmentalize a little better so I can be there for my students. They deserve my very best.

This struggle is even more of a reason why I should walk away and spend as much time as I can with Suzy. I'm glad Henry was ultimately supportive of my desire to step away. My mind is all over the place as I arrive home. I go through the back door and head straight for the bedroom.

Suzy sits up a bit and says, "Hey you. How's Meghan? Did y'all catch any fish?"

"She's great," I reply. "As usual, she had some very good questions. She is really doing a good job of noticing what happens around her. But like most of us, she has been quick to judge a few of her colleagues she perceived to be ineffective. She is learning that teaching can be a trying occupation, and some of us get to a point where we get so tired that we aren't very good teachers. I tried to help her understand that life gets in the way sometimes and affects our ability to be fully engaged with our students. We lose our passion for teaching and we are less effective."

I pause for a moment beside the bed, staring at my wife. "I honestly feel I am in that place right now. I know we haven't talked about it much, but I've been thinking about it and I am going to step away from teaching."

Suzy sits up a little further in the bed and says, "I don't want you to do that. You don't need to do that."

"I know I don't need to, but I want to do this. I want to be with you and help you in any way I can. It's something I truly want to do. I've talked to Henry and we have a plan. I told him I was going to retire, and he said I should take a leave of absence for the rest of the year, and we can re-evaluate over the summer. It's what I want to do. Please let me do this with you."

"Okay, Suzy says. "I love you."

CHAPTER 12

The Last Lesson: Catch and Release

Nathaniel

I rose early today before light as I always do on these Saturdays of fishing with Meghan. I really do look forward to these times with her on the water. While these past few months of Saturday mornings have been spent fishing and mentoring her, today there will be no fishing. Today will be different with us. It won't take her long to notice I didn't bring the boat today. She will know something's up. Today will be our last official mentoring session. And I'm not sure what I have to tell her, but I'm sure something will come to me as I explain what is going to happen next.

So, I sit here now watching as dawn breaks and shades of orange, pink, yellow, and red intertwine and brighten the morning sky. It's going to be a blue sky day. I've got a little while before she should arrive. I need this stillness today. To just sit on this dock and watch and think.

I've always loved that old Otis Redding song. The lyrics spoke to me years ago, and they speak to me again now: "Sittin' in the morning sun. I'll be sittin' when the evening comes. Watching the ships roll in. Then I watch them roll away again."

I want to hit the pause button and stop the future from invading. I want to sit here from morning sun until evening comes and just watch the boats come in and then leave again. I see myself as one of those boats today. The strange transition in my life between what was known into now what is unknown has thrown me for a loop. These past six weeks have felt like I've been living someone else's life. First, the realization that Suzy was so very sick and our time together might be cut short. Then, the conversation with Henry that I was going to take a leave of absence as of January 1st. The suddenness and sense of urgency with which I made the decision, the reasons for my departure, and the realization of what they would mean for Henry, were not lost on me. Although understanding and in agreement, I could see that this shook Henry. He would now be faced with finding a replacement as quickly as possible, shuffling other teachers' schedules around to best make up the gap, and explaining as best he could this situation to the rest of the teachers and students in the school. Even as I told him and he agreed that the decision and timing of this were mine and mine alone, I could not help but feel for him.

This week, in particular, has been hard. My mind has wandered, and I have found myself distracted throughout the day. The only place where I feel centered is at home with Suzy. She is the rock. Of course, I've seen Meghan these past few weeks and have been putting on the happy face in her presence. It's my way of coping. It's my way of being able to continue to be there for her. She has no idea what's coming, and I decided to wait to tell her until today. I am thinking we can just sit here on this dock and take in the stillness of the moment.

Meghan

Something is different. As I drive into the gravel parking lot excited about another beautiful morning of fishing with Nathaniel, I notice he is simply sitting on the dock. I slip into a parking space, turn off my car, and just sit there watching him for a few moments. Something is definitely different.

It looks like he's been there for some time. He is just staring out over the water and into the distance. The boat isn't here. He doesn't have the fishing gear he always brings.

I feel a small sense of uncertainty rise in my gut and realize that whatever today's lesson will be, it won't be what I've come to expect. I get out of the car and head over to where Nathaniel is sitting.

Nathaniel

Well, here she comes. It's time. The past hour watching the sunrise, being still, thinking, and waiting has been good. I'm ready now to send her on her way. I'm ready to release her.

"Good morning," I say.

"Good morning, Nathaniel. What's going on?"

That's all it took for her to say, and words begin pouring out of me. "Have a seat."

She sits down on the bench next to me and looks intently into my eyes, saying nothing but smiling nonetheless. I take a deep breath and return both her gaze and her smile. I feel a sense of contentment and peace in knowing that I am ready to tell her and she is ready to hear.

"We've come a long way over the past few months. I remember that first day I met you in the Back to School meeting in August. You were a bundle of energy and nerves. We went to lunch that day and I learned about who you were and what you hoped for. I remember my own excitement as I realized the opportunity that I would have to leave a legacy by working with you and mentoring you. This then proceeded into these wonderful Saturday morning fishing trips. Meghan, you pushed me with your questions to reflect on my own teaching career in a way that I hadn't truly done in my life. And although you may not have realized it, you taught me as much, if not more, than I taught you.

"Here's what I learned from you. I learned that we are never done. As long as we have life and breath, we are never done. There is always more we can learn, more we can do, and more that we can be. Thanks to you, I have learned more this year, done more this year, and become more this year. I want you to remember this. The reason this has happened is not because I wanted to mentor you. It happened through our relationship. My own need to continue to make a difference was met as I hopefully met your need to learn about the journey of becoming a teacher who makes a difference.

"Ultimately, teaching isn't something we do. Being a teacher is who we are. Whether you knew it or not, you were becoming a teacher long before I entered your life. And you will continue to grow and evolve as a teacher even as our lives go their separate ways for a while. And although it's now time for me to hit the pause button and put my formal teaching career on hold for now, I will always be a teacher learning along the way and hopefully continuing to make a difference in someone's life every day."

Meghan looks at me with confusion. "What do you mean by hitting the pause button and putting your formal teaching career on hold?"

"I'll explain what I meant by that in a minute," I say. "First, remember those exit slips I had you complete after each of our fishing expeditions? Well, as always there was a method to the madness of them beyond the takeaways and closure of our lessons together. I've been thinking a lot about our time together and the lessons we have both learned. We have alluded to various seasons that teachers experience during their careers, and given that we discussed them on a boat while fishing, it seems appropriate that we have nautical names for these various seasons.

"Remember the first one? That season of feeling overwhelming and exhausted? That season is the same as when the boat is *Swamped*. And then, as teachers, if we survive this season, we typically proceed into the *Smooth Sailing* season where rhythm, routine, and relationship have been established. But what I really want for you and for all teachers is to reach the next season, where you are *Full Speed Ahead*. This is where you feel like you are energized and 'on fire' for teaching. This is the place where you will truly make a difference, and where your impact will be felt not only by your students, but also by your fellow teachers, your school, the parents, your community, and also the profession of teaching. I also want you to remember that, with this stage in particular, there is a real need to make sure that you are sailing with an even keel, remembering to maintain balance in your life so as to be able to sustain this pace.

"We also talked about that time in a teacher's career where you might feel *Adrift* and simply going through the motions. Remember, this can occur when a teacher has entered a 'been there, done that' mentality and she feels there is nothing left to learn. I hope that if you ever feel this, that someone will be around to tell you the truth and give you a swift kick in the butt to find your true north again, remembering why you chose to become a teacher in the first place.

"And finally, remember that saddest season of teaching? This should be called the *Dead in the Water* season. This is that place of burnout. This is when teachers cannot care anymore. Something happens to them and they cease to care. For some, this is only temporary given life circumstances, and it becomes clear that their remaining energies need to be directed toward themselves. If this happens to you at some future point in your career, please apply for and take a sabbatical or a leave of absence from teaching. Then take the time needed to care for yourself so that you can return to the classroom and go back to making a difference. However, for some teachers, this stage is terminal and they need to leave teaching. If they stay, they are causing harm to students, to themselves, and to the profession."

Meghan

I am still and quiet as I listen to Nathaniel. He is serious and thoughtful as he seems to be summarizing everything that we've talked about while fishing over the past few months. But this is definitely different than how we usually interact. Besides the fact that we are sitting on a bench on a dock and not fishing, it feels almost as if he is saying goodbye. Clearly he has been thinking about this for a while. As I listen to every word, I feel like he is writing these words on my heart.

Yet, even as he pauses for a moment, there remains something unsaid between us. Something is coming, and I wonder what it is. Have I done something wrong? Is this our last fishing trip?

Nathaniel

"Just look out there, Meghan," I say. "Look at how beautiful this place is and remember all those moments where we caught those fish. Remember all the little celebrations we had too. I want you to remember all of our time together and all of the lessons learned here. Will you do that? Because, like all good things, these are coming to an end."

"What are you saying?" Meghan asks. "You keep hinting that you and I aren't going to have these fishing/mentoring meetings any more. Have I done something wrong? Why are you talking like you are going to walk away?"

"Here's the thing," I reply. "You've definitely done nothing wrong. I think we have developed a great friendship and learned from each other. I wanted to tell you this first before the rest of the teachers find out. I'm in fact taking a leave of absence. I will not be back after Christmas break. I have already spoken with Henry. Other than him, you and Suzy are the only ones who know."

"Why?" Meghan asks. "Are you sick? Are you injured or something?"

Tears begin to run down my cheeks. "To be with Suzy. She's really sick and I don't know what's going to happen or how long she might have to live. I found this out a little while back. I've been struggling with what to do and how to best handle it all. She's been diagnosed with stage 4 cancer and I'm truly scared for one of the few times in my life."

"I'm so sorry," Meghan says as tears begin to form in her eyes as well.

"Thanks, Meghan," I reply. We're at peace with it. Although it isn't anything that I would have predicted or planned for our lives, it is our reality and we both accept it. And you should know that part of accepting it is knowing that I can step away from that which I love. I can step away from teaching to help Suzy beat this thing and spend the rest of whatever time that we might have left together with absolute confidence, knowing that it is you who will carry on my legacy. It is you, Meghan, who will make a difference in so many lives now. It is you who have made this decision much easier for me. You know, I've always said, that when you are meant to know something, it will become made known to you. And you, Meghan, have been made known to me. I trust you with my students now and with all of those future students and teachers for whom you will make a difference."

I notice that it's raining very lightly. I have no idea how long it's been raining. We both sit there oblivious to it. I know this is hard for Meghan to hear. I've been thinking about how I might capture all that we've discussed during these incredible fishing trips. I want her to remember these lessons.

"I've tried to think of the best analogy for what is happening now," I say. "As I thought about it, I also realized that this is not only what is happening with us right now, but really is what the life of a teacher is all about. It's about *Catching and Releasing.* Just like what we've been doing these past few months while fly fishing on Saturday mornings. We as teachers are constantly catching and releasing our students. We find the right fly, we cast it into the water where we hope the fish will be, we wait to see if they will respond by rising, we feel them latch on as they take the fly, we set the hook, and then we experience the absolute beauty of reeling them in.

"Eventually, the time comes when, after we've landed them and they have been safely in our net, we gently remove the hook, carefully hold them in our hands and then release them to go home. Yes, teaching is about doing the same with our students. We release them to their future teachers. We prepare them for their future careers and lives. We help them build future relationships. We catch them for a while and we release them forever. Yes, some will return to us. Some will come back one day and thank us. And some will probably completely forget us. But for many of them, if we have done our work well of catching them and carefully teaching them, nurturing them, and loving them, then when we release them they will take all those lessons learned and remember us as they live out those lessons for years to come. That process is truly what it means to be a teacher who makes a difference.

"Meghan, it might sound a little quirky, but I realize that what is occurring now with us is also all about catching and releasing. Remember our somewhat awkward beginning when you literally ran right into me after the meeting and before we went to lunch? Remember that first conversation at Nell's Cafe? That 'getting to know you' moment where we began to share our stories? Remember when you first asked me how this whole mentoring thing was going to work? Well, quite honestly, I wasn't sure. I wasn't sure at all. All I knew for sure was that I wanted and needed to do this with you.

"I do not believe that our journey was random. I believe that both of us were exactly where we were supposed to be at exactly the moment that we were supposed to be there for such a time as this. I was able to catch and reel you in only because you responded to what I had to offer. I was able to mentor you these past few months and now, Meghan, it's time to release you. That is what we do. Whether it's students, or novice teachers, it's all the same.

"You are ready to do this thing on your own. I trust you to become the teacher that you were put on this earth to be. You don't have to be like any other teacher. You just have to be you. Because you were a good student, and working with you has been an incredible experience for me.

"It's also what I might have to do now with Suzy. It's obviously a different type of catch and release, but I caught her so many years ago. She caught me too. I remember our first meeting, dating, marrying her, and raising our kids together as if it were all yesterday. So many memories of being together and being safe and secure throughout all that life has given us over the years.

"Now, the hard part . . . she might beat this thing. But, I also want to be prepared to release her if it comes to that. She's the most important person in my life and that will make this releasing so much harder. But it is the natural way. I will carefully and gently care for her for as long as she has left. And then, if I have to, I will let her go.

"All of life is full of teachable moments as we catch and release. Keep learning them. Keep fine-tuning your craft."

There is nothing left to say. There is peace in these thoughts. So we sit. We watch. We cry. We hug. We smile. We say goodbye . . . for now.

Meghan

Wow, I've cried so much. My heart aches. My mind is whirling. My thoughts are scattered. Yet, I feel peaceful. I even feel joyful. Yes, sad for Nathaniel and prayerful for Suzy . . . yet joyful as well.

Although this meeting with Nathaniel was not at all what I expected or planned for, I will definitely remember it. Today, Nathaniel taught me not only what it means to teach, but what it means to live a life of significance. Although we had compared fly fishing to teaching a while ago, I wasn't ready or able to comprehend it further until just now. Because it's not just about the catching. It's more importantly about the releasing. How do we, as teachers, truly release our students to be prepared for whatever is next in their lives? The releasing is not the end. It is only the beginning of how they will hopefully take what we teach them and apply it.

As he said, Nathaniel is releasing me to become the teacher that hopefully changes lives in a positive way. He wants me to be me, rather than a female version of him. I do think I'm ready for this. Just like when we release a fish back into the water, sometimes it may take a moment or two for them to be on their way. They may struggle a little at first. But after a few moments, they are off. I imagine it will be like that for me. When I feel that uncertainty and that struggle, I will try to pause. I will breathe and find my way. I will remember Nathaniel and reflect on all the lessons he has taught me.

There will be other teachers and administrators to help me along the way. But, it will be different. I won't have Nathaniel to rely on. I liked his description of the seasons teachers tend to go through during their careers. Based on what I have noticed so far, we might not experience all of the seasons, but we all experience some of them. I believe, at some point, I will move past this feeling of being swamped and will experience smooth sailing. I know I will continually strive to go full speed ahead over the course of my career. I realize I may become adrift at times, but hopefully not ever become dead in the water. I will do this in part, because of Nathaniel's influence. And who knows. Maybe we will fish together again.

EXIT SLIP NUMBER SEVEN

1. *Sometimes life happens in ways you least expect.*
2. *Teachers go through seasons during their careers, and it's clear to me that I want to be self-aware enough to keep the welfare of my students in mind as I deal with my own insecurities or challenges that life might throw my way.*
3. *I am so blessed to have had Nathaniel in my life. He is the model all teachers should look to for inspiration and strategies for being a teacher who changes lives. Thank you, Nathaniel!*

References

Assiante, P. & Zug, J. (2010). *Run to the Roar: Coaching To Overcome Fear.* New York, NY: The Penguin Group.

Bass, B. (1990). *Bass and Stogdill's Handbook of Leadership: Theories, Research and Managerial Applications* (3rd ed.). New York, NY: The Free Press.

Brooks, M. (Producer), Brooks, M. (Director). *As Good as it Gets.* [Motion Picture]. United States: Gracie Films.

Duckworth, A. (2016). *Grit: The Power of Passion and Perseverance.* New York, NY: Scribner.

DuFour, R. (2011). A Bandwagon, An Idea Worth Considering, or Our Best Hope for High Levels of Learning? *Teacher Leadership: The "New" Foundations of Teacher Education,* 408, 159–164.

Gladwell, M. (2008). *Outliers.* New York, NY: Little, Brown and Company.

Farrell, B & P. (2001). *Men Are Like Waffles, Women Are like Spaghetti: Understanding and Delighting in your Differences.* Eugene, OR: Harvest House.

Jacobs, W. (1902). "The Monkey's Paw," in W. Jacobs (Ed.), *The lady of the Barge.* United Kingdom: Alan Rodgers Books.

Janssen, J. & Dale, G. *The Seven Secrets of Successful Coaches: How to Unlock and Unleash Your Team's Full Potential.* Cary, NC: Winning the Mental Game.

Marsh, N. (2009). *Overworked and Underlaid: A Seriously Funny Guide to Life.* Crows Nest, Australia: Arena Books.

Noddings, N. (2013). *Caring: A Relational Approach to Ethics and Moral Education (2nd ed.).* Berkeley, CA: University of California Press

Pausch, R. & Zaslow, J. (2008). *The Last Lecture: Lessons in Living.* New York, NY: Hyperion.

Redford, R. (Producer), Redford, R. (Director). (1992). *A River Runs through It.* [Motion Picture]. United States: Columbia Pictures.

Seligman, M. (2006). *Learned Optimism: How To Change Your Mind and Your Life.* New York, NY: Vintage Books.

About the Authors

Greg Dale

Greg spent his childhood in rural Texas and Alaska. Along the way, he had a couple of teachers who had a very positive impact on his life. As a result, he knew he wanted to teach in some capacity. He began his teaching career as an elementary science teacher in New York City. He has since taught at every level through graduate school. Hopefully, his love of teaching and his deep respect for what teachers do on a daily basis are revealed in the stories of Nathaniel and Meghan. Greg lives in Durham, NC with his wife, Cammie, and their children, Abbey, Graham, Jacob, and Luke.

Lynn Owens

From a struggling novice middle school physical education teacher to a successful tenured university professor in teacher education, Lynn Owens has impacted thousands of students and teachers over the span of thirty-nine years. A respected and sought after speaker, trainer, researcher, and educator, Lynn can be found either on a ranch in Montana that she shares with her husband, four horses, three mules, and a dog, or wandering around the country exploring out of the way places and packing into the wilderness.

Mark Thomas

Mark Thomas has spent the last fifteen years as the principal at Northview High School in Grand Rapids, Michigan. This year marked his thirtieth year as a public school educator. He began his career teaching English and speech courses at the high school level. His background also includes coaching at the high school and college levels. In 2010 Mark was honored by his peers as the Michigan Principal of the Year. He has served as the president of the Michigan Association of Secondary School Principals, as a board member of the Midwest Regional Education Laboratory and is currently the chair-elect of the Midwest Region for College Board.

Mark's wife Pam is also a public school educator. She is a highly successful elementary principal who previously served as a special education director and middle school teacher. They have three wonderful children, Kyle, Ethan, and Elizabeth.